ME/CFS WARRIOR

A tracking journal for
Myalgic encephalomyelitis /
Chronic fatigue syndrome

WELLNESS WARRIOR PRESS
www.wellnesswarriorpress.com

Copyright © 2021 by Wellness Warrior Press

ISBN: 978-1-990271-25-0

This journal belongs to...

_____

DOCTOR / SPECIALIST INFORMATION

Name	Address	Contact

DAILY MEDICATION / SUPPLEMENTS

Medication / Supplement	Dosage

Summary

For each journal entry, return to this summary page and
rate your overall sickness / fatigue / pain level
(1 being great and 10 being unbearable)

Entry #	Rating	Entry #	Rating
1		31	
2		32	
3		33	
4		34	
5		35	
6		36	
7		37	
8		38	
9		39	
10		40	
11		41	
12		42	
13		43	
14		44	
15		45	
16		46	
17		47	
18		48	
19		49	
20		50	
21		51	
22		52	
23		53	
24		54	
25		55	
26		56	
27		57	
28		58	
29		59	
30		60	

Date: 5/5/22

How are you feeling today?

Like death	Terrible	Not good	Meh	Good	Great!	Amazing!

PNI

97% am

RATE YOUR PAIN LEVEL

① ② ③(am) ④ ⑤ ⑥ ⑦ ⑧ ⑨ ⑩

TODAY'S SYMPTOMS

☑ Fatigue   ☐ Insomnia   ☑ Malaise

☑ Joint pain   ☐ Anxiety   ☐ Depression

☐ Muscle weakness   ☐ Muscle stiffness   ☐ Muscle aches

☐ Headache   ☐ Brain fog   ☐ Forgetfulness

☑ Blurred vision _____   ☐ _____

☐ _____   ☐ _____

Other symptoms:

_____

_____

WHAT ABOUT YOUR...?   **Feeling sick?**

Mood   ① ② ③ ④ ⑤ ⑥ ⑦ ⑧ ⑨ ⑩   ☑ Nope!

Energy levels   ① ② ③ ④ ⑤ ⑥ ⑦ ⑧ ⑨ ⑩   ☐ Yes...

Mental clarity ① ② ③ ④ ⑤ ⑥ ⑦ ⑧ ⑨ ⑩

☐ Nausea	☐ Diarrhea	☐ Vomiting	☐ Sore throat
☐ Congestion	☐ Coughing	☐ Chills	☐ Fever

Other symptoms: _____

LAST NIGHT'S SLEEP

Hours of Sleep ① ② ③ ④ ⑤ ⑥ ⑦ ⑧ (9) (10) (+)

Sleep Quality (1) (2) (3) (4) (5) (6) (7) (8) ⑨ (10)

STRESS LEVELS

Am

| None | Low | Medium | High | Max | @$#%! |

FOOD / MEDICATIONS

food / drinks	meds / supplements	time	dose
pancakes, egg turkey bacon Overnight oats strawberry cheesecake. pork chop peas mozz sticks snicker ice cream			

☑ usual daily medication

juice

answer forgot

8oz water ⟹ ① ② ③ (4) (5) (6) (7) (8) (9) (10)

caffeine ⟹ (1) (2) (3) (4) (5) (6) (7) (8) (9) (10)

alcohol ⟹ (1) (2) (3) (4) (5) (6) (7) (8) (9) (10)

EXERCISE / DAILY ACTIVITY

walk

☐ Heck yes, I worked out.

☑ I managed to exercise a bit.

☐ No, I haven't exercised at all.

☐ I did some stuff, and that counts.

DETAILS
shower in Am
went for pm
walk
fol well

NOTES / TRIGGERS / IMPROVEMENTS

Very stressful call mid afternoon - tanked mood, energy, etc.

I AM GRATEFUL FOR... having a back up plan

Date: 5/6/22

How are you feeling today?

Like death   Terrible   Not good   Meh   Good   Great!   Amazing!

77%

RATE YOUR PAIN LEVEL

(1) (2) ● (4) (5) (6) (7) (8) (9) (10)

TODAY'S SYMPTOMS		
☐ Fatigue	☐ Insomnia	☑ Malaise
☐ Joint pain	☑ Anxiety	☐ Depression
☐ Muscle weakness	☐ Muscle stiffness	☐ Muscle aches
☐ Headache	☐ Brain fog	☐ Forgetfulness
☐ _____	☐ _____	
☐ _____	☐ _____	

Other symptoms:

_____

WHAT ABOUT YOUR...?   Feeling sick?

Mood	(1)(2)(3)●(5)(6)(7)(8)(9)(10)	☐ Nope!
Energy levels	(1)(2)(3)(4)●(6)(7)(8)(9)(10)	☑ Yes...
Mental clarity	(1)(2)(3)(4)(5)(6)(7)●(9)(10)	

☑ Nausea	☐ Diarrhea	☐ Vomiting	☐ Sore throat
☐ Congestion	☐ Coughing	☐ Chills	☐ Fever

Other symptoms: _____

LAST NIGHT'S SLEEP

early shift and sam woke me @ 6am

Hours of Sleep (1) (2) (3) (4) **(5)** (6) (7) (8) (9) (10) (+)

Sleep Quality (1) (2) (3) **(4)** (5) (6) (7) (8) (9) (10)

STRESS LEVELS

None	Low	Medium	High	Max	@$#%!

FOOD / MEDICATIONS

food / drinks	meds / supplements	time	dose
cinnimon bagel			

☑ usual daily medication

water ⟹ **(1) (2) (3)** (4) (5) (6) (7) (8) (9) (10)

caffeine ⟹ (1) (2) (3) (4) (5) (6) (7) (8) (9) (10)

alcohol ⟹ (1) (2) (3) (4) (5) (6) (7) (8) (9) (10)

EXERCISE / DAILY ACTIVITY

☐ Heck yes, I worked out.

☐ I managed to exercise a bit.

☑ No, I haven't exercised at all.

☐ I did some stuff, and that counts.

DETAILS

NOTES / TRIGGERS / IMPROVEMENTS

I AM GRATEFUL FOR...

Date:_____

How are you feeling today?

Like death	Terrible	Not good	Meh	Good	Great!	Amazing!

RATE YOUR PAIN LEVEL

① ② ③ ④ ⑤ ⑥ ⑦ ⑧ ⑨ ⑩

TODAY'S SYMPTOMS

☐ Fatigue   ☐ Insomnia   ☐ Malaise

☐ Joint pain   ☐ Anxiety   ☐ Depression

☐ Muscle weakness ☐ Muscle stiffness ☐ Muscle aches

☐ Headache   ☐ Brain fog   ☐ Forgetfulness

☐ _____   ☐ _____

☐ _____   ☐ _____

Other symptoms:

_____

_____

WHAT ABOUT YOUR...?   **Feeling sick?**

Mood   ① ② ③ ④ ⑤ ⑥ ⑦ ⑧ ⑨ ⑩   ☐ Nope!

Energy levels   ① ② ③ ④ ⑤ ⑥ ⑦ ⑧ ⑨ ⑩   ☐ Yes...

Mental clarity ① ② ③ ④ ⑤ ⑥ ⑦ ⑧ ⑨ ⑩

☐ Nausea   ☐ Diarrhea   ☐ Vomiting   ☐ Sore throat

☐ Congestion   ☐ Coughing   ☐ Chills   ☐ Fever

Other symptoms: _____

LAST NIGHT'S SLEEP

Hours of Sleep ① ② ③ ④ ⑤ ⑥ ⑦ ⑧ ⑨ ⑩ ⊕

Sleep Quality ① ② ③ ④ ⑤ ⑥ ⑦ ⑧ ⑨ ⑩

STRESS LEVELS

None	Low	Medium	High	Max	@$#%!

FOOD / MEDICATIONS

food / drinks	*meds / supplements*	*time*	*dose*

☐ usual daily medication

water ⟹ ① ② ③ ④ ⑤ ⑥ ⑦ ⑧ ⑨ ⑩

caffeine ⟹ ① ② ③ ④ ⑤ ⑥ ⑦ ⑧ ⑨ ⑩

alcohol ⟹ ① ② ③ ④ ⑤ ⑥ ⑦ ⑧ ⑨ ⑩

EXERCISE / DAILY ACTIVITY

☐ Heck yes, I worked out.

☐ I managed to exercise a bit.

☐ No, I haven't exercised at all.

☐ I did some stuff, and that counts.

DETAILS

NOTES / TRIGGERS / IMPROVEMENTS

I AM GRATEFUL FOR...

Date: _____

How are you feeling today?

Like death	Terrible	Not good	Meh	Good	Great!	Amazing!

RATE YOUR PAIN LEVEL

(1) (2) (3) (4) (5) (6) (7) (8) (9) (10)

TODAY'S SYMPTOMS

☐ Fatigue   ☐ Insomnia   ☐ Malaise

☐ Joint pain   ☐ Anxiety   ☐ Depression

☐ Muscle weakness ☐ Muscle stiffness ☐ Muscle aches

☐ Headache   ☐ Brain fog   ☐ Forgetfulness

☐ _____   ☐ _____

☐ _____   ☐ _____

Other symptoms:
_____
_____

WHAT ABOUT YOUR...?

		Feeling sick?
Mood	①②③④⑤⑥⑦⑧⑨⑩	☐ Nope!
Energy levels	①②③④⑤⑥⑦⑧⑨⑩	☐ Yes...
Mental clarity	①②③④⑤⑥⑦⑧⑨⑩	

☐ Nausea   ☐ Diarrhea   ☐ Vomiting   ☐ Sore throat

☐ Congestion ☐ Coughing   ☐ Chills   ☐ Fever

Other symptoms: _____

LAST NIGHT'S SLEEP

Hours of Sleep (1) (2) (3) (4) (5) (6) (7) (8) (9) (10) (+)

Sleep Quality (1) (2) (3) (4) (5) (6) (7) (8) (9) (10)

STRESS LEVELS

None	Low	Medium	High	Max	@$#%!

FOOD / MEDICATIONS

food / drinks	meds / supplements	time	dose

☐ usual daily medication

water ⟹ (1) (2) (3) (4) (5) (6) (7) (8) (9) (10)

caffeine ⟹ (1) (2) (3) (4) (5) (6) (7) (8) (9) (10)

alcohol ⟹ (1) (2) (3) (4) (5) (6) (7) (8) (9) (10)

EXERCISE / DAILY ACTIVITY

☐ Heck yes, I worked out.

☐ I managed to exercise a bit.

☐ No, I haven't exercised at all.

☐ I did some stuff, and that counts.

DETAILS

NOTES / TRIGGERS / IMPROVEMENTS

I AM GRATEFUL FOR...

Date: _____

How are you feeling today?

Like death   Terrible   Not good   Meh   Good   Great!   Amazing!

RATE YOUR PAIN LEVEL

① ② ③ ④ ⑤ ⑥ ⑦ ⑧ ⑨ ⑩

TODAY'S SYMPTOMS

☐ Fatigue   ☐ Insomnia   ☐ Malaise

☐ Joint pain   ☐ Anxiety   ☐ Depression

☐ Muscle weakness   ☐ Muscle stiffness ☐ Muscle aches

☐ Headache   ☐ Brain fog   ☐ Forgetfulness

☐ _____ ☐ _____

☐ _____ ☐ _____

Other symptoms:

WHAT ABOUT YOUR...?   Feeling sick?

Mood   ① ② ③ ④ ⑤ ⑥ ⑦ ⑧ ⑨ ⑩   ☐ Nope!

Energy levels ① ② ③ ④ ⑤ ⑥ ⑦ ⑧ ⑨ ⑩   ☐ Yes...

Mental clarity ① ② ③ ④ ⑤ ⑥ ⑦ ⑧ ⑨ ⑩

☐ Nausea   ☐ Diarrhea   ☐ Vomiting   ☐ Sore throat

☐ Congestion   ☐ Coughing   ☐ Chills   ☐ Fever

Other symptoms: _____

LAST NIGHT'S SLEEP

Hours of Sleep (1) (2) (3) (4) (5) (6) (7) (8) (9) (10) (+)

Sleep Quality (1) (2) (3) (4) (5) (6) (7) (8) (9) (10)

STRESS LEVELS

None	Low	Medium	High	Max	@$#%!

FOOD / MEDICATIONS

food / drinks	meds / supplements	time	dose

☐ usual daily medication

water ⟹ (1) (2) (3) (4) (5) (6) (7) (8) (9) (10)

caffeine ⟹ (1) (2) (3) (4) (5) (6) (7) (8) (9) (10)

alcohol ⟹ (1) (2) (3) (4) (5) (6) (7) (8) (9) (10)

EXERCISE / DAILY ACTIVITY

☐ Heck yes, I worked out.

☐ I managed to exercise a bit.

☐ No, I haven't exercised at all.

☐ I did some stuff, and that counts.

DETAILS

NOTES / TRIGGERS / IMPROVEMENTS

I AM GRATEFUL FOR…

Date: _____

How are you feeling today?

Like death	Terrible	Not good	Meh	Good	Great!	Amazing!

RATE YOUR PAIN LEVEL

① ② ③ ④ ⑤ ⑥ ⑦ ⑧ ⑨ ⑩

TODAY'S SYMPTOMS

☐ Fatigue   ☐ Insomnia   ☐ Malaise

☐ Joint pain   ☐ Anxiety   ☐ Depression

☐ Muscle weakness ☐ Muscle stiffness ☐ Muscle aches

☐ Headache   ☐ Brain fog   ☐ Forgetfulness

☐ _____   ☐ _____

☐ _____   ☐ _____

Other symptoms:

_____

_____

WHAT ABOUT YOUR...?   **Feeling sick?**

Mood	① ② ③ ④ ⑤ ⑥ ⑦ ⑧ ⑨ ⑩	☐ Nope!
Energy levels	① ② ③ ④ ⑤ ⑥ ⑦ ⑧ ⑨ ⑩	☐ Yes...
Mental clarity	① ② ③ ④ ⑤ ⑥ ⑦ ⑧ ⑨ ⑩	

☐ Nausea   ☐ Diarrhea   ☐ Vomiting   ☐ Sore throat

☐ Congestion ☐ Coughing   ☐ Chills   ☐ Fever

Other symptoms: _____

LAST NIGHT'S SLEEP

Hours of Sleep ① ② ③ ④ ⑤ ⑥ ⑦ ⑧ ⑨ ⑩ ⊕

Sleep Quality ① ② ③ ④ ⑤ ⑥ ⑦ ⑧ ⑨ ⑩

STRESS LEVELS

None	Low	Medium	High	Max	@$#%!

FOOD / MEDICATIONS

food / drinks	meds / supplements	time	dose

☐ usual daily medication

water ⟹ ① ② ③ ④ ⑤ ⑥ ⑦ ⑧ ⑨ ⑩

caffeine ⟹ ① ② ③ ④ ⑤ ⑥ ⑦ ⑧ ⑨ ⑩

alcohol ⟹ ① ② ③ ④ ⑤ ⑥ ⑦ ⑧ ⑨ ⑩

EXERCISE / DAILY ACTIVITY

☐ Heck yes, I worked out.

☐ I managed to exercise a bit.

☐ No, I haven't exercised at all.

☐ I did some stuff, and that counts.

DETAILS

NOTES / TRIGGERS / IMPROVEMENTS

I AM GRATEFUL FOR…

Date: _____

How are you feeling today?

Like death	Terrible	Not good	Meh	Good	Great!	Amazing!

RATE YOUR PAIN LEVEL

(1) (2) (3) (4) (5) (6) (7) (8) (9) (10)

TODAY'S SYMPTOMS

☐ Fatigue   ☐ Insomnia   ☐ Malaise

☐ Joint pain   ☐ Anxiety   ☐ Depression

☐ Muscle weakness ☐ Muscle stiffness ☐ Muscle aches

☐ Headache   ☐ Brain fog   ☐ Forgetfulness

☐ _____   ☐ _____

☐ _____   ☐ _____

Other symptoms:

WHAT ABOUT YOUR...?

		Feeling sick?
Mood	(1)(2)(3)(4)(5)(6)(7)(8)(9)(10)	☐ Nope!
Energy levels	(1)(2)(3)(4)(5)(6)(7)(8)(9)(10)	☐ Yes...
Mental clarity	(1)(2)(3)(4)(5)(6)(7)(8)(9)(10)	

☐ Nausea   ☐ Diarrhea   ☐ Vomiting   ☐ Sore throat

☐ Congestion ☐ Coughing   ☐ Chills   ☐ Fever

Other symptoms: _____

LAST NIGHT'S SLEEP

Hours of Sleep (1) (2) (3) (4) (5) (6) (7) (8) (9) (10) (+)

Sleep Quality (1) (2) (3) (4) (5) (6) (7) (8) (9) (10)

STRESS LEVELS

None	Low	Medium	High	Max	@$#%!

FOOD / MEDICATIONS

food / drinks	meds / supplements	time	dose

☐ usual daily medication

water → (1) (2) (3) (4) (5) (6) (7) (8) (9) (10)

caffeine → (1) (2) (3) (4) (5) (6) (7) (8) (9) (10)

alcohol → (1) (2) (3) (4) (5) (6) (7) (8) (9) (10)

EXERCISE / DAILY ACTIVITY

☐ Heck yes, I worked out.

☐ I managed to exercise a bit.

☐ No, I haven't exercised at all.

☐ I did some stuff, and that counts.

DETAILS

NOTES / TRIGGERS / IMPROVEMENTS

I AM GRATEFUL FOR...

Date:_____

How are you feeling today?

Like death   Terrible   Not good   Meh   Good   Great!   Amazing!

RATE YOUR PAIN LEVEL

① ② ③ ④ ⑤ ⑥ ⑦ ⑧ ⑨ ⑩

TODAY'S SYMPTOMS

☐ Fatigue ☐ Insomnia ☐ Malaise

☐ Joint pain ☐ Anxiety ☐ Depression

☐ Muscle weakness ☐ Muscle stiffness ☐ Muscle aches

☐ Headache ☐ Brain fog ☐ Forgetfulness

☐ _____ ☐ _____

☐ _____ ☐ _____

Other symptoms:

_____

_____

WHAT ABOUT YOUR...?

Mood   ① ② ③ ④ ⑤ ⑥ ⑦ ⑧ ⑨ ⑩

Energy levels   ① ② ③ ④ ⑤ ⑥ ⑦ ⑧ ⑨ ⑩

Mental clarity   ① ② ③ ④ ⑤ ⑥ ⑦ ⑧ ⑨ ⑩

Feeling sick?

☐ Nope!

☐ Yes...

☐ Nausea ☐ Diarrhea ☐ Vomiting ☐ Sore throat

☐ Congestion ☐ Coughing ☐ Chills ☐ Fever

Other symptoms: _____

LAST NIGHT'S SLEEP

Hours of Sleep (1) (2) (3) (4) (5) (6) (7) (8) (9) (10) (+)

Sleep Quality (1) (2) (3) (4) (5) (6) (7) (8) (9) (10)

STRESS LEVELS

None	Low	Medium	High	Max	@$#%!

FOOD / MEDICATIONS

food / drinks	meds / supplements	time	dose

☐ usual daily medication

water ⟹ (1) (2) (3) (4) (5) (6) (7) (8) (9) (10)

caffeine ⟹ (1) (2) (3) (4) (5) (6) (7) (8) (9) (10)

alcohol ⟹ (1) (2) (3) (4) (5) (6) (7) (8) (9) (10)

EXERCISE / DAILY ACTIVITY

☐ Heck yes, I worked out.

☐ I managed to exercise a bit.

☐ No, I haven't exercised at all.

☐ I did some stuff, and that counts.

DETAILS

NOTES / TRIGGERS / IMPROVEMENTS

I AM GRATEFUL FOR...

Date: _____

How are you feeling today?

Like death	Terrible	Not good	Meh	Good	Great!	Amazing!

RATE YOUR PAIN LEVEL

① ② ③ ④ ⑤ ⑥ ⑦ ⑧ ⑨ ⑩

TODAY'S SYMPTOMS

☐ Fatigue ☐ Insomnia ☐ Malaise

☐ Joint pain ☐ Anxiety ☐ Depression

☐ Muscle weakness ☐ Muscle stiffness ☐ Muscle aches

☐ Headache ☐ Brain fog ☐ Forgetfulness

☐ _____ ☐ _____

☐ _____ ☐ _____

Other symptoms:

_____

_____

WHAT ABOUT YOUR...?   Feeling sick?

Mood   ① ② ③ ④ ⑤ ⑥ ⑦ ⑧ ⑨ ⑩   ☐   Nope!

Energy levels   ① ② ③ ④ ⑤ ⑥ ⑦ ⑧ ⑨ ⑩   ☐   Yes...

Mental clarity ① ② ③ ④ ⑤ ⑥ ⑦ ⑧ ⑨ ⑩

☐ Nausea   ☐ Diarrhea   ☐ Vomiting   ☐ Sore throat

☐ Congestion ☐ Coughing   ☐ Chills   ☐ Fever

Other symptoms: _____

LAST NIGHT'S SLEEP

Hours of Sleep ① ② ③ ④ ⑤ ⑥ ⑦ ⑧ ⑨ ⑩ ⊕

Sleep Quality ① ② ③ ④ ⑤ ⑥ ⑦ ⑧ ⑨ ⑩

STRESS LEVELS

None	Low	Medium	High	Max	@$#%!

FOOD / MEDICATIONS

food / drinks	meds / supplements	time	dose

☐ usual daily medication

water ⟹ ① ② ③ ④ ⑤ ⑥ ⑦ ⑧ ⑨ ⑩

caffeine ⟹ ① ② ③ ④ ⑤ ⑥ ⑦ ⑧ ⑨ ⑩

alcohol ⟹ ① ② ③ ④ ⑤ ⑥ ⑦ ⑧ ⑨ ⑩

EXERCISE / DAILY ACTIVITY

☐ Heck yes, I worked out.

☐ I managed to exercise a bit.

☐ No, I haven't exercised at all.

☐ I did some stuff, and that counts.

DETAILS

NOTES / TRIGGERS / IMPROVEMENTS

I AM GRATEFUL FOR...

Date:_____

How are you feeling today?

Like death	Terrible	Not good	Meh	Good	Great!	Amazing!

RATE YOUR PAIN LEVEL

(1) (2) (3) (4) (5) (6) (7) (8) (9) (10)

TODAY'S SYMPTOMS

☐ Fatigue   ☐ Insomnia   ☐ Malaise

☐ Joint pain   ☐ Anxiety   ☐ Depression

☐ Muscle weakness ☐ Muscle stiffness ☐ Muscle aches

☐ Headache   ☐ Brain fog   ☐ Forgetfulness

☐ _____   ☐ _____

☐ _____   ☐ _____

Other symptoms:

_____

_____

WHAT ABOUT YOUR...?   **Feeling sick?**

Mood   (1)(2)(3)(4)(5)(6)(7)(8)(9)(10)   ☐ Nope!

Energy levels   (1)(2)(3)(4)(5)(6)(7)(8)(9)(10)   ☐ Yes...

Mental clarity (1)(2)(3)(4)(5)(6)(7)(8)(9)(10)

| ☐ Nausea | ☐ Diarrhea | ☐ Vomiting | ☐ Sore throat |
| ☐ Congestion | ☐ Coughing | ☐ Chills | ☐ Fever |

Other symptoms: _____

LET'S EXPLORE SOME MORE

LAST NIGHT'S SLEEP

Hours of Sleep   ① ② ③ ④ ⑤ ⑥ ⑦ ⑧ ⑨ ⑩ ⊕

Sleep Quality   ① ② ③ ④ ⑤ ⑥ ⑦ ⑧ ⑨ ⑩

STRESS LEVELS

None	Low	Medium	High	Max	@$#%!

FOOD / MEDICATIONS

food / drinks	meds / supplements	time	dose

☐ usual daily medication

water ➡ ① ② ③ ④ ⑤ ⑥ ⑦ ⑧ ⑨ ⑩

caffeine ➡ ① ② ③ ④ ⑤ ⑥ ⑦ ⑧ ⑨ ⑩

alcohol ➡ ① ② ③ ④ ⑤ ⑥ ⑦ ⑧ ⑨ ⑩

EXERCISE / DAILY ACTIVITY

☐   Heck yes, I worked out.

☐   I managed to exercise a bit.

☐   No, I haven't exercised at all.

☐   I did some stuff, and that counts.

DETAILS

NOTES / TRIGGERS / IMPROVEMENTS

I AM GRATEFUL FOR...

Date: _____

How are you feeling today?

| Like death | Terrible | Not good | Meh | Good | Great! | Amazing! |

RATE YOUR PAIN LEVEL

① ② ③ ④ ⑤ ⑥ ⑦ ⑧ ⑨ ⑩

TODAY'S SYMPTOMS

☐ Fatigue   ☐ Insomnia   ☐ Malaise

☐ Joint pain   ☐ Anxiety   ☐ Depression

☐ Muscle weakness ☐ Muscle stiffness ☐ Muscle aches

☐ Headache   ☐ Brain fog   ☐ Forgetfulness

☐ _____   ☐ _____

☐ _____   ☐ _____

Other symptoms:

_____

WHAT ABOUT YOUR...?   Feeling sick?

Mood   ① ② ③ ④ ⑤ ⑥ ⑦ ⑧ ⑨ ⑩   ☐ Nope!
Energy levels   ① ② ③ ④ ⑤ ⑥ ⑦ ⑧ ⑨ ⑩   ☐ Yes...
Mental clarity ① ② ③ ④ ⑤ ⑥ ⑦ ⑧ ⑨ ⑩

☐ Nausea   ☐ Diarrhea   ☐ Vomiting   ☐ Sore throat
☐ Congestion   ☐ Coughing   ☐ Chills   ☐ Fever

Other symptoms: _____

LET'S EXPLORE SOME MORE #11

LAST NIGHT'S SLEEP

Hours of Sleep ① ② ③ ④ ⑤ ⑥ ⑦ ⑧ ⑨ ⑩ ⊕

Sleep Quality ① ② ③ ④ ⑤ ⑥ ⑦ ⑧ ⑨ ⑩

STRESS LEVELS

None	Low	Medium	High	Max	@$#%!

FOOD / MEDICATIONS

food / drinks	meds / supplements	time	dose

☐ usual daily medication

water ① ② ③ ④ ⑤ ⑥ ⑦ ⑧ ⑨ ⑩

caffeine ① ② ③ ④ ⑤ ⑥ ⑦ ⑧ ⑨ ⑩

alcohol ① ② ③ ④ ⑤ ⑥ ⑦ ⑧ ⑨ ⑩

EXERCISE / DAILY ACTIVITY

☐ Heck yes, I worked out.

☐ I managed to exercise a bit.

☐ No, I haven't exercised at all.

☐ I did some stuff, and that counts.

DETAILS

NOTES / TRIGGERS / IMPROVEMENTS

I AM GRATEFUL FOR...

Date:_____

How are you feeling today?

Like death	Terrible	Not good	Meh	Good	Great!	Amazing!

RATE YOUR PAIN LEVEL

(1) (2) (3) (4) (5) (6) (7) (8) (9) (10)

TODAY'S SYMPTOMS

☐ Fatigue   ☐ Insomnia   ☐ Malaise

☐ Joint pain   ☐ Anxiety   ☐ Depression

☐ Muscle weakness   ☐ Muscle stiffness   ☐ Muscle aches

☐ Headache   ☐ Brain fog   ☐ Forgetfulness

☐ _____   ☐ _____

☐ _____   ☐ _____

Other symptoms:

_____

_____

WHAT ABOUT YOUR...?

Mood   (1) (2) (3) (4) (5) (6) (7) (8) (9) (10)

Energy levels   (1) (2) (3) (4) (5) (6) (7) (8) (9) (10)

Mental clarity   (1) (2) (3) (4) (5) (6) (7) (8) (9) (10)

Feeling sick?

☐ Nope!

☐ Yes...

☐ Nausea   ☐ Diarrhea   ☐ Vomiting   ☐ Sore throat

☐ Congestion   ☐ Coughing   ☐ Chills   ☐ Fever

Other symptoms: _____

LAST NIGHT'S SLEEP

Hours of Sleep (1) (2) (3) (4) (5) (6) (7) (8) (9) (10) (+)

Sleep Quality (1) (2) (3) (4) (5) (6) (7) (8) (9) (10)

STRESS LEVELS

None	Low	Medium	High	Max	@$#%!

FOOD / MEDICATIONS

food / drinks	*meds / supplements*	*time*	*dose*

☐ usual daily medication

water ➡ (1) (2) (3) (4) (5) (6) (7) (8) (9) (10)

caffeine ➡ (1) (2) (3) (4) (5) (6) (7) (8) (9) (10)

alcohol ➡ (1) (2) (3) (4) (5) (6) (7) (8) (9) (10)

EXERCISE / DAILY ACTIVITY

☐ Heck yes, I worked out.

☐ I managed to exercise a bit.

☐ No, I haven't exercised at all.

☐ I did some stuff, and that counts.

DETAILS

NOTES / TRIGGERS / IMPROVEMENTS

I AM GRATEFUL FOR...

Date:_____

How are you feeling today?

Like death | Terrible | Not good | Meh | Good | Great! | Amazing!

RATE YOUR PAIN LEVEL

① ② ③ ④ ⑤ ⑥ ⑦ ⑧ ⑨ ⑩

TODAY'S SYMPTOMS

☐ Fatigue ☐ Insomnia ☐ Malaise

☐ Joint pain ☐ Anxiety ☐ Depression

☐ Muscle weakness ☐ Muscle stiffness ☐ Muscle aches

☐ Headache ☐ Brain fog ☐ Forgetfulness

☐ _____ ☐ _____

☐ _____ ☐ _____

Other symptoms:

_____

_____

WHAT ABOUT YOUR...?   **Feeling sick?**

Mood   ① ② ③ ④ ⑤ ⑥ ⑦ ⑧ ⑨ ⑩   ☐ Nope!

Energy levels   ① ② ③ ④ ⑤ ⑥ ⑦ ⑧ ⑨ ⑩   ☐ Yes...

Mental clarity ① ② ③ ④ ⑤ ⑥ ⑦ ⑧ ⑨ ⑩

☐ Nausea   ☐ Diarrhea   ☐ Vomiting   ☐ Sore throat

☐ Congestion ☐ Coughing   ☐ Chills   ☐ Fever

Other symptoms: _____

LET'S EXPLORE SOME MORE #13

LAST NIGHT'S SLEEP

Hours of Sleep ① ② ③ ④ ⑤ ⑥ ⑦ ⑧ ⑨ ⑩ ⊕

Sleep Quality ① ② ③ ④ ⑤ ⑥ ⑦ ⑧ ⑨ ⑩

STRESS LEVELS

None	Low	Medium	High	Max	@$#%!

FOOD / MEDICATIONS

food / drinks	meds / supplements	time	dose

☐ usual daily medication

water ⟹ ① ② ③ ④ ⑤ ⑥ ⑦ ⑧ ⑨ ⑩

caffeine ⟹ ① ② ③ ④ ⑤ ⑥ ⑦ ⑧ ⑨ ⑩

alcohol ⟹ ① ② ③ ④ ⑤ ⑥ ⑦ ⑧ ⑨ ⑩

EXERCISE / DAILY ACTIVITY

☐ Heck yes, I worked out.

☐ I managed to exercise a bit.

☐ No, I haven't exercised at all.

☐ I did some stuff, and that counts.

DETAILS

NOTES / TRIGGERS / IMPROVEMENTS

I AM GRATEFUL FOR...

Date: _____

How are you feeling today?

Like death   Terrible   Not good   Meh   Good   Great!   Amazing!

RATE YOUR PAIN LEVEL

(1) (2) (3) (4) (5) (6) (7) (8) (9) (10)

TODAY'S SYMPTOMS

☐ Fatigue   ☐ Insomnia   ☐ Malaise

☐ Joint pain   ☐ Anxiety   ☐ Depression

☐ Muscle weakness ☐ Muscle stiffness ☐ Muscle aches

☐ Headache   ☐ Brain fog   ☐ Forgetfulness

☐ _____   ☐ _____

☐ _____   ☐ _____

Other symptoms:

WHAT ABOUT YOUR...?

Mood	(1)(2)(3)(4)(5)(6)(7)(8)(9)(10)
Energy levels	(1)(2)(3)(4)(5)(6)(7)(8)(9)(10)
Mental clarity	(1)(2)(3)(4)(5)(6)(7)(8)(9)(10)

Feeling sick?

☐ Nope!

☐ Yes...

☐ Nausea   ☐ Diarrhea   ☐ Vomiting   ☐ Sore throat
☐ Congestion   ☐ Coughing   ☐ Chills   ☐ Fever

Other symptoms: _____

LET'S EXPLORE SOME MORE #14

LAST NIGHT'S SLEEP

Hours of Sleep (1)(2)(3)(4)(5)(6)(7)(8)(9)(10)(+)

Sleep Quality (1)(2)(3)(4)(5)(6)(7)(8)(9)(10)

STRESS LEVELS

None	Low	Medium	High	Max	@$#%!

FOOD / MEDICATIONS

food / drinks	meds / supplements	time	dose

☐ usual daily medication

water ⟹ (1)(2)(3)(4)(5)(6)(7)(8)(9)(10)

caffeine ⟹ (1)(2)(3)(4)(5)(6)(7)(8)(9)(10)

alcohol ⟹ (1)(2)(3)(4)(5)(6)(7)(8)(9)(10)

EXERCISE / DAILY ACTIVITY

☐ Heck yes, I worked out.

☐ I managed to exercise a bit.

☐ No, I haven't exercised at all.

☐ I did some stuff, and that counts.

DETAILS

NOTES / TRIGGERS / IMPROVEMENTS

I AM GRATEFUL FOR...

Date:_____

How are you feeling today?

| Like death | Terrible | Not good | Meh | Good | Great! | Amazing! |

RATE YOUR PAIN LEVEL

① ② ③ ④ ⑤ ⑥ ⑦ ⑧ ⑨ ⑩

TODAY'S SYMPTOMS

☐ Fatigue ☐ Insomnia ☐ Malaise

☐ Joint pain ☐ Anxiety ☐ Depression

☐ Muscle weakness ☐ Muscle stiffness ☐ Muscle aches

☐ Headache ☐ Brain fog ☐ Forgetfulness

☐ _____ ☐ _____

☐ _____ ☐ _____

Other symptoms:
_____
_____

WHAT ABOUT YOUR...?   **Feeling sick?**

Mood   ① ② ③ ④ ⑤ ⑥ ⑦ ⑧ ⑨ ⑩   ☐ Nope!

Energy levels   ① ② ③ ④ ⑤ ⑥ ⑦ ⑧ ⑨ ⑩   ☐ Yes...

Mental clarity ① ② ③ ④ ⑤ ⑥ ⑦ ⑧ ⑨ ⑩

☐ Nausea ☐ Diarrhea ☐ Vomiting ☐ Sore throat

☐ Congestion ☐ Coughing ☐ Chills ☐ Fever

Other symptoms: _____

LAST NIGHT'S SLEEP

Hours of Sleep   ① ② ③ ④ ⑤ ⑥ ⑦ ⑧ ⑨ ⑩ ⊕

Sleep Quality   ① ② ③ ④ ⑤ ⑥ ⑦ ⑧ ⑨ ⑩

STRESS LEVELS

None	Low	Medium	High	Max	@$#%!

FOOD / MEDICATIONS

food / drinks	meds / supplements	time	dose

☐ usual daily medication

water	⟹	① ② ③ ④ ⑤ ⑥ ⑦ ⑧ ⑨ ⑩
caffeine	⟹	① ② ③ ④ ⑤ ⑥ ⑦ ⑧ ⑨ ⑩
alcohol	⟹	① ② ③ ④ ⑤ ⑥ ⑦ ⑧ ⑨ ⑩

EXERCISE / DAILY ACTIVITY

☐ Heck yes, I worked out.

☐ I managed to exercise a bit.

☐ No, I haven't exercised at all.

☐ I did some stuff, and that counts.

NOTES / TRIGGERS / IMPROVEMENTS

DETAILS

I AM GRATEFUL FOR...

Date: _____

How are you feeling today?

Like death	Terrible	Not good	Meh	Good	Great!	Amazing!

RATE YOUR PAIN LEVEL

(1) (2) (3) (4) (5) (6) (7) (8) (9) (10)

TODAY'S SYMPTOMS

☐ Fatigue   ☐ Insomnia   ☐ Malaise

☐ Joint pain   ☐ Anxiety   ☐ Depression

☐ Muscle weakness   ☐ Muscle stiffness   ☐ Muscle aches

☐ Headache   ☐ Brain fog   ☐ Forgetfulness

☐ _____   ☐ _____

☐ _____   ☐ _____

Other symptoms:

_____

_____

WHAT ABOUT YOUR...?

Feeling sick?

Mood   (1)(2)(3)(4)(5)(6)(7)(8)(9)(10)   ☐ Nope!

Energy levels   (1)(2)(3)(4)(5)(6)(7)(8)(9)(10)   ☐ Yes...

Mental clarity   (1)(2)(3)(4)(5)(6)(7)(8)(9)(10)

☐ Nausea   ☐ Diarrhea   ☐ Vomiting   ☐ Sore throat

☐ Congestion   ☐ Coughing   ☐ Chills   ☐ Fever

Other symptoms: _____

LAST NIGHT'S SLEEP

Hours of Sleep ① ② ③ ④ ⑤ ⑥ ⑦ ⑧ ⑨ ⑩ ⊕

Sleep Quality ① ② ③ ④ ⑤ ⑥ ⑦ ⑧ ⑨ ⑩

STRESS LEVELS

None	Low	Medium	High	Max	@$#%!

FOOD / MEDICATIONS

food / drinks	meds / supplements	time	dose

☐ usual daily medication

water ① ② ③ ④ ⑤ ⑥ ⑦ ⑧ ⑨ ⑩

caffeine ① ② ③ ④ ⑤ ⑥ ⑦ ⑧ ⑨ ⑩

alcohol ① ② ③ ④ ⑤ ⑥ ⑦ ⑧ ⑨ ⑩

EXERCISE / DAILY ACTIVITY

☐ Heck yes, I worked out.

☐ I managed to exercise a bit.

☐ No, I haven't exercised at all.

☐ I did some stuff, and that counts.

DETAILS

NOTES / TRIGGERS / IMPROVEMENTS

I AM GRATEFUL FOR...

Date: _____

How are you feeling today?

Like death	Terrible	Not good	Meh	Good	Great!	Amazing!

RATE YOUR PAIN LEVEL

(1) (2) (3) (4) (5) (6) (7) (8) (9) (10)

TODAY'S SYMPTOMS

☐ Fatigue	☐ Insomnia	☐ Malaise
☐ Joint pain	☐ Anxiety	☐ Depression
☐ Muscle weakness	☐ Muscle stiffness	☐ Muscle aches
☐ Headache	☐ Brain fog	☐ Forgetfulness

☐ _____   ☐ _____

☐ _____   ☐ _____

Other symptoms:

_____

WHAT ABOUT YOUR...?

Feeling sick?

Mood   (1) (2) (3) (4) (5) (6) (7) (8) (9) (10)   ☐ Nope!

Energy levels (1) (2) (3) (4) (5) (6) (7) (8) (9) (10)   ☐ Yes...

Mental clarity (1) (2) (3) (4) (5) (6) (7) (8) (9) (10)

☐ Nausea	☐ Diarrhea	☐ Vomiting	☐ Sore throat
☐ Congestion	☐ Coughing	☐ Chills	☐ Fever

Other symptoms: _____

LAST NIGHT'S SLEEP

Hours of Sleep (1) (2) (3) (4) (5) (6) (7) (8) (9) (10) (+)

Sleep Quality (1) (2) (3) (4) (5) (6) (7) (8) (9) (10)

STRESS LEVELS

None	Low	Medium	High	Max	@$#%!

FOOD / MEDICATIONS

food / drinks	meds / supplements	time	dose

☐ usual daily medication

water → (1) (2) (3) (4) (5) (6) (7) (8) (9) (10)

caffeine → (1) (2) (3) (4) (5) (6) (7) (8) (9) (10)

alcohol → (1) (2) (3) (4) (5) (6) (7) (8) (9) (10)

EXERCISE / DAILY ACTIVITY

☐ Heck yes, I worked out.

☐ I managed to exercise a bit.

☐ No, I haven't exercised at all.

☐ I did some stuff, and that counts.

DETAILS

NOTES / TRIGGERS / IMPROVEMENTS

I AM GRATEFUL FOR...

Date: _____

How are you feeling today?

Like death	Terrible	Not good	Meh	Good	Great!	Amazing!

RATE YOUR PAIN LEVEL

① ② ③ ④ ⑤ ⑥ ⑦ ⑧ ⑨ ⑩

TODAY'S SYMPTOMS

☐ Fatigue ☐ Insomnia ☐ Malaise

☐ Joint pain ☐ Anxiety ☐ Depression

☐ Muscle weakness ☐ Muscle stiffness ☐ Muscle aches

☐ Headache ☐ Brain fog ☐ Forgetfulness

☐ _____ ☐ _____

☐ _____ ☐ _____

Other symptoms:

_____

_____

WHAT ABOUT YOUR...?   **Feeling sick?**

Mood   ① ② ③ ④ ⑤ ⑥ ⑦ ⑧ ⑨ ⑩   ☐ Nope!

Energy levels   ① ② ③ ④ ⑤ ⑥ ⑦ ⑧ ⑨ ⑩   ☐ Yes...

Mental clarity ① ② ③ ④ ⑤ ⑥ ⑦ ⑧ ⑨ ⑩

☐ Nausea   ☐ Diarrhea   ☐ Vomiting   ☐ Sore throat

☐ Congestion ☐ Coughing   ☐ Chills   ☐ Fever

Other symptoms: _____

LET'S EXPLORE SOME MORE #18

LAST NIGHT'S SLEEP

Hours of Sleep (1)(2)(3)(4)(5)(6)(7)(8)(9)(10)(+)

Sleep Quality (1)(2)(3)(4)(5)(6)(7)(8)(9)(10)

STRESS LEVELS

None	Low	Medium	High	Max	@$#%!

FOOD / MEDICATIONS

food / drinks	meds / supplements	time	dose

☐ usual daily medication

water ⟹ (1)(2)(3)(4)(5)(6)(7)(8)(9)(10)

caffeine ⟹ (1)(2)(3)(4)(5)(6)(7)(8)(9)(10)

alcohol ⟹ (1)(2)(3)(4)(5)(6)(7)(8)(9)(10)

EXERCISE / DAILY ACTIVITY

☐ Heck yes, I worked out.

☐ I managed to exercise a bit.

☐ No, I haven't exercised at all.

☐ I did some stuff, and that counts.

DETAILS

NOTES / TRIGGERS / IMPROVEMENTS

I AM GRATEFUL FOR…

Date: _____

How are you feeling today?

Like death · Terrible · Not good · Meh · Good · Great! · Amazing!

RATE YOUR PAIN LEVEL

① ② ③ ④ ⑤ ⑥ ⑦ ⑧ ⑨ ⑩

TODAY'S SYMPTOMS

☐ Fatigue   ☐ Insomnia   ☐ Malaise

☐ Joint pain   ☐ Anxiety   ☐ Depression

☐ Muscle weakness ☐ Muscle stiffness ☐ Muscle aches

☐ Headache   ☐ Brain fog   ☐ Forgetfulness

☐ _____   ☐ _____

☐ _____   ☐ _____

Other symptoms:
_____
_____

WHAT ABOUT YOUR...?

Mood   ① ② ③ ④ ⑤ ⑥ ⑦ ⑧ ⑨ ⑩
Energy levels ① ② ③ ④ ⑤ ⑥ ⑦ ⑧ ⑨ ⑩
Mental clarity ① ② ③ ④ ⑤ ⑥ ⑦ ⑧ ⑨ ⑩

Feeling sick?

☐ Nope!
☐ Yes...

☐ Nausea   ☐ Diarrhea   ☐ Vomiting   ☐ Sore throat
☐ Congestion ☐ Coughing   ☐ Chills   ☐ Fever

Other symptoms: _____

LET'S EXPLORE SOME MORE #19

LAST NIGHT'S SLEEP

Hours of Sleep ① ② ③ ④ ⑤ ⑥ ⑦ ⑧ ⑨ ⑩ ⊕

Sleep Quality ① ② ③ ④ ⑤ ⑥ ⑦ ⑧ ⑨ ⑩

STRESS LEVELS

None	Low	Medium	High	Max	@$#%!

FOOD / MEDICATIONS

food / drinks	meds / supplements	time	dose

☐ usual daily medication

water ➡ ① ② ③ ④ ⑤ ⑥ ⑦ ⑧ ⑨ ⑩

caffeine ➡ ① ② ③ ④ ⑤ ⑥ ⑦ ⑧ ⑨ ⑩

alcohol ➡ ① ② ③ ④ ⑤ ⑥ ⑦ ⑧ ⑨ ⑩

EXERCISE / DAILY ACTIVITY

☐ Heck yes, I worked out.

☐ I managed to exercise a bit.

☐ No, I haven't exercised at all.

☐ I did some stuff, and that counts.

DETAILS

NOTES / TRIGGERS / IMPROVEMENTS

I AM GRATEFUL FOR...

Date: _____

How are you feeling today?

| Like death | Terrible | Not good | Meh | Good | Great! | Amazing! |

RATE YOUR PAIN LEVEL

① ② ③ ④ ⑤ ⑥ ⑦ ⑧ ⑨ ⑩

TODAY'S SYMPTOMS

☐ Fatigue   ☐ Insomnia   ☐ Malaise

☐ Joint pain   ☐ Anxiety   ☐ Depression

☐ Muscle weakness ☐ Muscle stiffness ☐ Muscle aches

☐ Headache   ☐ Brain fog   ☐ Forgetfulness

☐ _____   ☐ _____

☐ _____   ☐ _____

Other symptoms:

_____

WHAT ABOUT YOUR...?   Feeling sick?

Mood	① ② ③ ④ ⑤ ⑥ ⑦ ⑧ ⑨ ⑩	☐ Nope!
Energy levels	① ② ③ ④ ⑤ ⑥ ⑦ ⑧ ⑨ ⑩	☐ Yes...
Mental clarity	① ② ③ ④ ⑤ ⑥ ⑦ ⑧ ⑨ ⑩	

☐ Nausea   ☐ Diarrhea   ☐ Vomiting   ☐ Sore throat
☐ Congestion   ☐ Coughing   ☐ Chills   ☐ Fever

Other symptoms: _____

LAST NIGHT'S SLEEP

Hours of Sleep ① ② ③ ④ ⑤ ⑥ ⑦ ⑧ ⑨ ⑩ ⊕

Sleep Quality ① ② ③ ④ ⑤ ⑥ ⑦ ⑧ ⑨ ⑩

STRESS LEVELS

None	Low	Medium	High	Max	@$#%!

FOOD / MEDICATIONS

food / drinks	meds / supplements	time	dose

☐ usual daily medication

water ① ② ③ ④ ⑤ ⑥ ⑦ ⑧ ⑨ ⑩

caffeine ① ② ③ ④ ⑤ ⑥ ⑦ ⑧ ⑨ ⑩

alcohol ① ② ③ ④ ⑤ ⑥ ⑦ ⑧ ⑨ ⑩

EXERCISE / DAILY ACTIVITY

☐ Heck yes, I worked out.

☐ I managed to exercise a bit.

☐ No, I haven't exercised at all.

☐ I did some stuff, and that counts.

NOTES / TRIGGERS / IMPROVEMENTS

DETAILS

I AM GRATEFUL FOR...

Date: _____

How are you feeling today?

Like death	Terrible	Not good	Meh	Good	Great!	Amazing!

RATE YOUR PAIN LEVEL

(1) (2) (3) (4) (5) (6) (7) (8) (9) (10)

TODAY'S SYMPTOMS

☐ Fatigue   ☐ Insomnia   ☐ Malaise

☐ Joint pain   ☐ Anxiety   ☐ Depression

☐ Muscle weakness   ☐ Muscle stiffness   ☐ Muscle aches

☐ Headache   ☐ Brain fog   ☐ Forgetfulness

☐ _____   ☐ _____

☐ _____   ☐ _____

Other symptoms:

_____

_____

WHAT ABOUT YOUR...?   **Feeling sick?**

Mood	(1)(2)(3)(4)(5)(6)(7)(8)(9)(10)	☐ Nope!
Energy levels	(1)(2)(3)(4)(5)(6)(7)(8)(9)(10)	☐ Yes...
Mental clarity	(1)(2)(3)(4)(5)(6)(7)(8)(9)(10)	

☐ Nausea   ☐ Diarrhea   ☐ Vomiting   ☐ Sore throat

☐ Congestion   ☐ Coughing   ☐ Chills   ☐ Fever

Other symptoms: _____

LET'S EXPLORE SOME MORE #21

LAST NIGHT'S SLEEP

Hours of Sleep ① ② ③ ④ ⑤ ⑥ ⑦ ⑧ ⑨ ⑩ ⊕

Sleep Quality ① ② ③ ④ ⑤ ⑥ ⑦ ⑧ ⑨ ⑩

STRESS LEVELS

None	Low	Medium	High	Max	@$#%!

FOOD / MEDICATIONS

food / drinks	meds / supplements	time	dose

☐ usual daily medication

water ① ② ③ ④ ⑤ ⑥ ⑦ ⑧ ⑨ ⑩

caffeine ① ② ③ ④ ⑤ ⑥ ⑦ ⑧ ⑨ ⑩

alcohol ① ② ③ ④ ⑤ ⑥ ⑦ ⑧ ⑨ ⑩

EXERCISE / DAILY ACTIVITY

☐ Heck yes, I worked out.

☐ I managed to exercise a bit.

☐ No, I haven't exercised at all.

☐ I did some stuff, and that counts.

DETAILS

NOTES / TRIGGERS / IMPROVEMENTS

I AM GRATEFUL FOR…

Date: _____

How are you feeling today?

Like death	Terrible	Not good	Meh	Good	Great!	Amazing!

RATE YOUR PAIN LEVEL

(1) (2) (3) (4) (5) (6) (7) (8) (9) (10)

TODAY'S SYMPTOMS

☐ Fatigue ☐ Insomnia ☐ Malaise

☐ Joint pain ☐ Anxiety ☐ Depression

☐ Muscle weakness ☐ Muscle stiffness ☐ Muscle aches

☐ Headache ☐ Brain fog ☐ Forgetfulness

☐ _____ ☐ _____

☐ _____ ☐ _____

Other symptoms:

_____

_____

WHAT ABOUT YOUR...?   Feeling sick?

Mood   (1) (2) (3) (4) (5) (6) (7) (8) (9) (10)   ☐ Nope!

Energy levels (1) (2) (3) (4) (5) (6) (7) (8) (9) (10)   ☐ Yes...

Mental clarity (1) (2) (3) (4) (5) (6) (7) (8) (9) (10)

☐ Nausea   ☐ Diarrhea   ☐ Vomiting   ☐ Sore throat

☐ Congestion ☐ Coughing   ☐ Chills   ☐ Fever

Other symptoms: _____

LAST NIGHT'S SLEEP

Hours of Sleep   ① ② ③ ④ ⑤ ⑥ ⑦ ⑧ ⑨ ⑩ ⊕

Sleep Quality   ① ② ③ ④ ⑤ ⑥ ⑦ ⑧ ⑨ ⑩

STRESS LEVELS

None	Low	Medium	High	Max	@$#%!

FOOD / MEDICATIONS

food / drinks	meds / supplements	time	dose

☐ usual daily medication

water ⟹ ① ② ③ ④ ⑤ ⑥ ⑦ ⑧ ⑨ ⑩

caffeine ⟹ ① ② ③ ④ ⑤ ⑥ ⑦ ⑧ ⑨ ⑩

alcohol ⟹ ① ② ③ ④ ⑤ ⑥ ⑦ ⑧ ⑨ ⑩

EXERCISE / DAILY ACTIVITY

☐ Heck yes, I worked out.

☐ I managed to exercise a bit.

☐ No, I haven't exercised at all.

☐ I did some stuff, and that counts.

DETAILS

NOTES / TRIGGERS / IMPROVEMENTS

I AM GRATEFUL FOR...

Date: _____

How are you feeling today?

| Like death | Terrible | Not good | Meh | Good | Great! | Amazing! |

RATE YOUR PAIN LEVEL

(1) (2) (3) (4) (5) (6) (7) (8) (9) (10)

TODAY'S SYMPTOMS

☐ Fatigue   ☐ Insomnia   ☐ Malaise

☐ Joint pain   ☐ Anxiety   ☐ Depression

☐ Muscle weakness ☐ Muscle stiffness ☐ Muscle aches

☐ Headache   ☐ Brain fog   ☐ Forgetfulness

☐ _____   ☐ _____

☐ _____   ☐ _____

Other symptoms:
_____
_____

WHAT ABOUT YOUR...?   **Feeling sick?**

Mood   (1)(2)(3)(4)(5)(6)(7)(8)(9)(10)   ☐ Nope!

Energy levels   (1)(2)(3)(4)(5)(6)(7)(8)(9)(10)   ☐ Yes...

Mental clarity (1)(2)(3)(4)(5)(6)(7)(8)(9)(10)

☐ Nausea   ☐ Diarrhea   ☐ Vomiting   ☐ Sore throat
☐ Congestion   ☐ Coughing   ☐ Chills   ☐ Fever

Other symptoms: _____

LET'S EXPLORE SOME MORE #23

LAST NIGHT'S SLEEP

Hours of Sleep   ① ② ③ ④ ⑤ ⑥ ⑦ ⑧ ⑨ ⑩ ⊕

Sleep Quality   ① ② ③ ④ ⑤ ⑥ ⑦ ⑧ ⑨ ⑩

STRESS LEVELS

None	Low	Medium	High	Max	@$#%!

FOOD / MEDICATIONS

food / drinks	meds / supplements	time	dose

☐ usual daily medication

water → ① ② ③ ④ ⑤ ⑥ ⑦ ⑧ ⑨ ⑩

caffeine → ① ② ③ ④ ⑤ ⑥ ⑦ ⑧ ⑨ ⑩

alcohol → ① ② ③ ④ ⑤ ⑥ ⑦ ⑧ ⑨ ⑩

EXERCISE / DAILY ACTIVITY

☐ Heck yes, I worked out.

☐ I managed to exercise a bit.

☐ No, I haven't exercised at all.

☐ I did some stuff, and that counts.

DETAILS

NOTES / TRIGGERS / IMPROVEMENTS

I AM GRATEFUL FOR...

Date: _____

How are you feeling today?

Like death	Terrible	Not good	Meh	Good	Great!	Amazing!

RATE YOUR PAIN LEVEL

(1) (2) (3) (4) (5) (6) (7) (8) (9) (10)

TODAY'S SYMPTOMS

☐ Fatigue   ☐ Insomnia   ☐ Malaise

☐ Joint pain   ☐ Anxiety   ☐ Depression

☐ Muscle weakness ☐ Muscle stiffness ☐ Muscle aches

☐ Headache   ☐ Brain fog   ☐ Forgetfulness

☐ _____   ☐ _____

☐ _____   ☐ _____

Other symptoms:

_____

_____

WHAT ABOUT YOUR...?   **Feeling sick?**

Mood   (1) (2) (3) (4) (5) (6) (7) (8) (9) (10)   ☐ Nope!

Energy levels   (1) (2) (3) (4) (5) (6) (7) (8) (9) (10)   ☐ Yes...

Mental clarity (1) (2) (3) (4) (5) (6) (7) (8) (9) (10)

☐ Nausea   ☐ Diarrhea   ☐ Vomiting   ☐ Sore throat

☐ Congestion   ☐ Coughing   ☐ Chills   ☐ Fever

Other symptoms: _____

LET'S EXPLORE SOME MORE #24

LAST NIGHT'S SLEEP

Hours of Sleep ① ② ③ ④ ⑤ ⑥ ⑦ ⑧ ⑨ ⑩ ⊕

Sleep Quality ① ② ③ ④ ⑤ ⑥ ⑦ ⑧ ⑨ ⑩

STRESS LEVELS

None	Low	Medium	High	Max	@$#%!

FOOD / MEDICATIONS

food / drinks	meds / supplements	time	dose

☐ usual daily medication

water → ① ② ③ ④ ⑤ ⑥ ⑦ ⑧ ⑨ ⑩

caffeine → ① ② ③ ④ ⑤ ⑥ ⑦ ⑧ ⑨ ⑩

alcohol → ① ② ③ ④ ⑤ ⑥ ⑦ ⑧ ⑨ ⑩

EXERCISE / DAILY ACTIVITY

☐ Heck yes, I worked out.

☐ I managed to exercise a bit.

☐ No, I haven't exercised at all.

☐ I did some stuff, and that counts.

DETAILS

NOTES / TRIGGERS / IMPROVEMENTS

I AM GRATEFUL FOR...

Date: _____

How are you feeling today?

| Like death | Terrible | Not good | Meh | Good | Great! | Amazing! |

RATE YOUR PAIN LEVEL

① ② ③ ④ ⑤ ⑥ ⑦ ⑧ ⑨ ⑩

TODAY'S SYMPTOMS

☐ Fatigue   ☐ Insomnia   ☐ Malaise

☐ Joint pain   ☐ Anxiety   ☐ Depression

☐ Muscle weakness ☐ Muscle stiffness ☐ Muscle aches

☐ Headache   ☐ Brain fog   ☐ Forgetfulness

☐ _____   ☐ _____

☐ _____   ☐ _____

Other symptoms:

_____

_____

WHAT ABOUT YOUR...?   **Feeling sick?**

Mood	① ② ③ ④ ⑤ ⑥ ⑦ ⑧ ⑨ ⑩	☐ Nope!
Energy levels	① ② ③ ④ ⑤ ⑥ ⑦ ⑧ ⑨ ⑩	☐ Yes...
Mental clarity	① ② ③ ④ ⑤ ⑥ ⑦ ⑧ ⑨ ⑩	

☐ Nausea   ☐ Diarrhea   ☐ Vomiting   ☐ Sore throat

☐ Congestion   ☐ Coughing   ☐ Chills   ☐ Fever

Other symptoms: _____

LET'S EXPLORE SOME MORE #25

LAST NIGHT'S SLEEP

Hours of Sleep (1) (2) (3) (4) (5) (6) (7) (8) (9) (10) (+)

Sleep Quality (1) (2) (3) (4) (5) (6) (7) (8) (9) (10)

STRESS LEVELS

None	Low	Medium	High	Max	@$#%!

FOOD / MEDICATIONS

food / drinks	meds / supplements	time	dose

☐ usual daily medication

water ⟹ (1) (2) (3) (4) (5) (6) (7) (8) (9) (10)

caffeine ⟹ (1) (2) (3) (4) (5) (6) (7) (8) (9) (10)

alcohol ⟹ (1) (2) (3) (4) (5) (6) (7) (8) (9) (10)

EXERCISE / DAILY ACTIVITY

☐ Heck yes, I worked out.

☐ I managed to exercise a bit.

☐ No, I haven't exercised at all.

☐ I did some stuff, and that counts.

DETAILS

NOTES / TRIGGERS / IMPROVEMENTS

I AM GRATEFUL FOR...

Date: _____

How are you feeling today?

Like death	Terrible	Not good	Meh	Good	Great!	Amazing!

RATE YOUR PAIN LEVEL

① ② ③ ④ ⑤ ⑥ ⑦ ⑧ ⑨ ⑩

TODAY'S SYMPTOMS

☐ Fatigue　　　　☐ Insomnia　　　☐ Malaise

☐ Joint pain　　　☐ Anxiety　　　　☐ Depression

☐ Muscle weakness　☐ Muscle stiffness　☐ Muscle aches

☐ Headache　　　☐ Brain fog　　　☐ Forgetfulness

☐ _____　　☐ _____

☐ _____　　☐ _____

Other symptoms:

_____

WHAT ABOUT YOUR...?　　　　　　　Feeling sick?

Mood　　　　　① ② ③ ④ ⑤ ⑥ ⑦ ⑧ ⑨ ⑩　☐ Nope!

Energy levels　① ② ③ ④ ⑤ ⑥ ⑦ ⑧ ⑨ ⑩　☐ Yes...

Mental clarity　① ② ③ ④ ⑤ ⑥ ⑦ ⑧ ⑨ ⑩

☐ Nausea　　　☐ Diarrhea　　☐ Vomiting　　☐ Sore throat

☐ Congestion　☐ Coughing　　☐ Chills　　　☐ Fever

Other symptoms: _____

LET'S EXPLORE SOME MORE #26

LAST NIGHT'S SLEEP

Hours of Sleep ① ② ③ ④ ⑤ ⑥ ⑦ ⑧ ⑨ ⑩ ⊕

Sleep Quality ① ② ③ ④ ⑤ ⑥ ⑦ ⑧ ⑨ ⑩

STRESS LEVELS

None	Low	Medium	High	Max	@$#%!

FOOD / MEDICATIONS

food / drinks	meds / supplements	time	dose

☐ usual daily medication

water ① ② ③ ④ ⑤ ⑥ ⑦ ⑧ ⑨ ⑩

caffeine ① ② ③ ④ ⑤ ⑥ ⑦ ⑧ ⑨ ⑩

alcohol ① ② ③ ④ ⑤ ⑥ ⑦ ⑧ ⑨ ⑩

EXERCISE / DAILY ACTIVITY

☐ Heck yes, I worked out.

☐ I managed to exercise a bit.

☐ No, I haven't exercised at all.

☐ I did some stuff, and that counts.

DETAILS

NOTES / TRIGGERS / IMPROVEMENTS

I AM GRATEFUL FOR...

Date: _____

How are you feeling today?

Like death	Terrible	Not good	Meh	Good	Great!	Amazing!

RATE YOUR PAIN LEVEL

(1) (2) (3) (4) (5) (6) (7) (8) (9) (10)

TODAY'S SYMPTOMS

☐ Fatigue ☐ Insomnia ☐ Malaise

☐ Joint pain ☐ Anxiety ☐ Depression

☐ Muscle weakness ☐ Muscle stiffness ☐ Muscle aches

☐ Headache ☐ Brain fog ☐ Forgetfulness

☐ _____ ☐ _____

☐ _____ ☐ _____

Other symptoms: _____

_____

_____

WHAT ABOUT YOUR...?

Feeling sick?

Mood (1) (2) (3) (4) (5) (6) (7) (8) (9) (10) ☐ Nope!

Energy levels (1) (2) (3) (4) (5) (6) (7) (8) (9) (10) ☐ Yes...

Mental clarity (1) (2) (3) (4) (5) (6) (7) (8) (9) (10)

☐ Nausea ☐ Diarrhea ☐ Vomiting ☐ Sore throat

☐ Congestion ☐ Coughing ☐ Chills ☐ Fever

Other symptoms: _____

LET'S EXPLORE SOME MORE

LAST NIGHT'S SLEEP

Hours of Sleep (1) (2) (3) (4) (5) (6) (7) (8) (9) (10) (+)

Sleep Quality (1) (2) (3) (4) (5) (6) (7) (8) (9) (10)

STRESS LEVELS

None	Low	Medium	High	Max	@$#%!

FOOD / MEDICATIONS

food / drinks	meds / supplements	time	dose

☐ usual daily medication

water ⟹ (1) (2) (3) (4) (5) (6) (7) (8) (9) (10)

caffeine ⟹ (1) (2) (3) (4) (5) (6) (7) (8) (9) (10)

alcohol ⟹ (1) (2) (3) (4) (5) (6) (7) (8) (9) (10)

EXERCISE / DAILY ACTIVITY

☐ Heck yes, I worked out.

☐ I managed to exercise a bit.

☐ No, I haven't exercised at all.

☐ I did some stuff, and that counts.

DETAILS

NOTES / TRIGGERS / IMPROVEMENTS

I AM GRATEFUL FOR...

Date: _____

How are you feeling today?

Like death   Terrible   Not good   Meh   Good   Great!   Amazing!

RATE YOUR PAIN LEVEL

(1) (2) (3) (4) (5) (6) (7) (8) (9) (10)

TODAY'S SYMPTOMS

☐ Fatigue   ☐ Insomnia   ☐ Malaise

☐ Joint pain   ☐ Anxiety   ☐ Depression

☐ Muscle weakness   ☐ Muscle stiffness   ☐ Muscle aches

☐ Headache   ☐ Brain fog   ☐ Forgetfulness

☐ _____   ☐ _____

☐ _____   ☐ _____

Other symptoms:
_____
_____

WHAT ABOUT YOUR...?

Feeling sick?

Mood   (1) (2) (3) (4) (5) (6) (7) (8) (9) (10)   ☐ Nope!

Energy levels   (1) (2) (3) (4) (5) (6) (7) (8) (9) (10)   ☐ Yes...

Mental clarity   (1) (2) (3) (4) (5) (6) (7) (8) (9) (10)

☐ Nausea   ☐ Diarrhea   ☐ Vomiting   ☐ Sore throat

☐ Congestion   ☐ Coughing   ☐ Chills   ☐ Fever

Other symptoms: _____

LAST NIGHT'S SLEEP

Hours of Sleep (1) (2) (3) (4) (5) (6) (7) (8) (9) (10) (+)

Sleep Quality (1) (2) (3) (4) (5) (6) (7) (8) (9) (10)

STRESS LEVELS

None	Low	Medium	High	Max	@$#%!

FOOD / MEDICATIONS

food / drinks	meds / supplements	time	dose

☐ usual daily medication

water ⟹ (1) (2) (3) (4) (5) (6) (7) (8) (9) (10)

caffeine ⟹ (1) (2) (3) (4) (5) (6) (7) (8) (9) (10)

alcohol ⟹ (1) (2) (3) (4) (5) (6) (7) (8) (9) (10)

EXERCISE / DAILY ACTIVITY

☐ Heck yes, I worked out.

☐ I managed to exercise a bit.

☐ No, I haven't exercised at all.

☐ I did some stuff, and that counts.

DETAILS

NOTES / TRIGGERS / IMPROVEMENTS

I AM GRATEFUL FOR...

Date:_____

How are you feeling today?

| Like death | Terrible | Not good | Meh | Good | Great! | Amazing! |

RATE YOUR PAIN LEVEL

(1) (2) (3) (4) (5) (6) (7) (8) (9) (10)

TODAY'S SYMPTOMS

☐ Fatigue	☐ Insomnia	☐ Malaise
☐ Joint pain	☐ Anxiety	☐ Depression
☐ Muscle weakness	☐ Muscle stiffness	☐ Muscle aches
☐ Headache	☐ Brain fog	☐ Forgetfulness

☐ _____   ☐ _____

☐ _____   ☐ _____

Other symptoms:

_____

WHAT ABOUT YOUR...?   **Feeling sick?**

Mood   (1)(2)(3)(4)(5)(6)(7)(8)(9)(10)   ☐   Nope!

Energy levels   (1)(2)(3)(4)(5)(6)(7)(8)(9)(10)   ☐   Yes...

Mental clarity (1)(2)(3)(4)(5)(6)(7)(8)(9)(10)

| ☐ Nausea | ☐ Diarrhea | ☐ Vomiting | ☐ Sore throat |
| ☐ Congestion | ☐ Coughing | ☐ Chills | ☐ Fever |

Other symptoms: _____

LET'S EXPLORE SOME MORE #29

LAST NIGHT'S SLEEP

Hours of Sleep ① ② ③ ④ ⑤ ⑥ ⑦ ⑧ ⑨ ⑩ ⊕

Sleep Quality ① ② ③ ④ ⑤ ⑥ ⑦ ⑧ ⑨ ⑩

STRESS LEVELS

None	Low	Medium	High	Max	@$#%!

FOOD / MEDICATIONS

food / drinks	meds / supplements	time	dose

☐ usual daily medication

water ① ② ③ ④ ⑤ ⑥ ⑦ ⑧ ⑨ ⑩

caffeine ① ② ③ ④ ⑤ ⑥ ⑦ ⑧ ⑨ ⑩

alcohol ① ② ③ ④ ⑤ ⑥ ⑦ ⑧ ⑨ ⑩

EXERCISE / DAILY ACTIVITY

☐ Heck yes, I worked out.

☐ I managed to exercise a bit.

☐ No, I haven't exercised at all.

☐ I did some stuff, and that counts.

DETAILS

NOTES / TRIGGERS / IMPROVEMENTS

I AM GRATEFUL FOR...

Date: _____

How are you feeling today?

Like death	Terrible	Not good	Meh	Good	Great!	Amazing!

RATE YOUR PAIN LEVEL

① ② ③ ④ ⑤ ⑥ ⑦ ⑧ ⑨ ⑩

TODAY'S SYMPTOMS

☐ Fatigue ☐ Insomnia ☐ Malaise

☐ Joint pain ☐ Anxiety ☐ Depression

☐ Muscle weakness ☐ Muscle stiffness ☐ Muscle aches

☐ Headache ☐ Brain fog ☐ Forgetfulness

☐ _____ ☐ _____

☐ _____ ☐ _____

Other symptoms:

_____

_____

WHAT ABOUT YOUR...?

Mood	① ② ③ ④ ⑤ ⑥ ⑦ ⑧ ⑨ ⑩
Energy levels	① ② ③ ④ ⑤ ⑥ ⑦ ⑧ ⑨ ⑩
Mental clarity	① ② ③ ④ ⑤ ⑥ ⑦ ⑧ ⑨ ⑩

Feeling sick?

☐ Nope!

☐ Yes...

☐ Nausea ☐ Diarrhea ☐ Vomiting ☐ Sore throat

☐ Congestion ☐ Coughing ☐ Chills ☐ Fever

Other symptoms: _____

LET'S EXPLORE SOME MORE #30

LAST NIGHT'S SLEEP

Hours of Sleep ① ② ③ ④ ⑤ ⑥ ⑦ ⑧ ⑨ ⑩ ⊕

Sleep Quality ① ② ③ ④ ⑤ ⑥ ⑦ ⑧ ⑨ ⑩

STRESS LEVELS

None	Low	Medium	High	Max	@$#%!

FOOD / MEDICATIONS

food / drinks	meds / supplements	time	dose

☐ usual daily medication

water ⟹ ① ② ③ ④ ⑤ ⑥ ⑦ ⑧ ⑨ ⑩

caffeine ⟹ ① ② ③ ④ ⑤ ⑥ ⑦ ⑧ ⑨ ⑩

alcohol ⟹ ① ② ③ ④ ⑤ ⑥ ⑦ ⑧ ⑨ ⑩

EXERCISE / DAILY ACTIVITY

☐ Heck yes, I worked out.

☐ I managed to exercise a bit.

☐ No, I haven't exercised at all.

☐ I did some stuff, and that counts.

DETAILS

NOTES / TRIGGERS / IMPROVEMENTS

I AM GRATEFUL FOR...

Date: _____

How are you feeling today?

| Like death | Terrible | Not good | Meh | Good | Great! | Amazing! |

RATE YOUR PAIN LEVEL

① ② ③ ④ ⑤ ⑥ ⑦ ⑧ ⑨ ⑩

TODAY'S SYMPTOMS

☐ Fatigue   ☐ Insomnia   ☐ Malaise

☐ Joint pain   ☐ Anxiety   ☐ Depression

☐ Muscle weakness   ☐ Muscle stiffness   ☐ Muscle aches

☐ Headache   ☐ Brain fog   ☐ Forgetfulness

☐ _____   ☐ _____

☐ _____   ☐ _____

Other symptoms:

_____

_____

WHAT ABOUT YOUR...?   ## Feeling sick?

Mood   ① ② ③ ④ ⑤ ⑥ ⑦ ⑧ ⑨ ⑩   ☐ Nope!

Energy levels ① ② ③ ④ ⑤ ⑥ ⑦ ⑧ ⑨ ⑩   ☐ Yes...

Mental clarity ① ② ③ ④ ⑤ ⑥ ⑦ ⑧ ⑨ ⑩

☐ Nausea   ☐ Diarrhea   ☐ Vomiting   ☐ Sore throat

☐ Congestion   ☐ Coughing   ☐ Chills   ☐ Fever

Other symptoms: _____

LET'S EXPLORE SOME MORE #31

LAST NIGHT'S SLEEP

Hours of Sleep ① ② ③ ④ ⑤ ⑥ ⑦ ⑧ ⑨ ⑩ ⊕

Sleep Quality ① ② ③ ④ ⑤ ⑥ ⑦ ⑧ ⑨ ⑩

STRESS LEVELS

None	Low	Medium	High	Max	@$#%!

FOOD / MEDICATIONS

food / drinks	meds / supplements	time	dose

☐ usual daily medication

water ① ② ③ ④ ⑤ ⑥ ⑦ ⑧ ⑨ ⑩

caffeine ① ② ③ ④ ⑤ ⑥ ⑦ ⑧ ⑨ ⑩

alcohol ① ② ③ ④ ⑤ ⑥ ⑦ ⑧ ⑨ ⑩

EXERCISE / DAILY ACTIVITY

☐ Heck yes, I worked out.

☐ I managed to exercise a bit.

☐ No, I haven't exercised at all.

☐ I did some stuff, and that counts.

DETAILS

NOTES / TRIGGERS / IMPROVEMENTS

I AM GRATEFUL FOR…

Date: _____

How are you feeling today?

Like death	Terrible	Not good	Meh	Good	Great!	Amazing!

RATE YOUR PAIN LEVEL

① ② ③ ④ ⑤ ⑥ ⑦ ⑧ ⑨ ⑩

TODAY'S SYMPTOMS

☐ Fatigue   ☐ Insomnia   ☐ Malaise

☐ Joint pain   ☐ Anxiety   ☐ Depression

☐ Muscle weakness ☐ Muscle stiffness ☐ Muscle aches

☐ Headache   ☐ Brain fog   ☐ Forgetfulness

☐ _____   ☐ _____

☐ _____   ☐ _____

Other symptoms:

WHAT ABOUT YOUR...?   **Feeling sick?**

Mood   ① ② ③ ④ ⑤ ⑥ ⑦ ⑧ ⑨ ⑩   ☐   Nope!

Energy levels   ① ② ③ ④ ⑤ ⑥ ⑦ ⑧ ⑨ ⑩   ☐   Yes...

Mental clarity ① ② ③ ④ ⑤ ⑥ ⑦ ⑧ ⑨ ⑩

☐ Nausea   ☐ Diarrhea   ☐ Vomiting   ☐ Sore throat

☐ Congestion ☐ Coughing   ☐ Chills   ☐ Fever

Other symptoms: _____

LET'S EXPLORE SOME MORE #32

LAST NIGHT'S SLEEP

Hours of Sleep ① ② ③ ④ ⑤ ⑥ ⑦ ⑧ ⑨ ⑩ ⊕

Sleep Quality ① ② ③ ④ ⑤ ⑥ ⑦ ⑧ ⑨ ⑩

STRESS LEVELS

None	Low	Medium	High	Max	@$#%!

FOOD / MEDICATIONS

food / drinks	meds / supplements	time	dose

☐ usual daily medication

water ⟹ ① ② ③ ④ ⑤ ⑥ ⑦ ⑧ ⑨ ⑩

caffeine ⟹ ① ② ③ ④ ⑤ ⑥ ⑦ ⑧ ⑨ ⑩

alcohol ⟹ ① ② ③ ④ ⑤ ⑥ ⑦ ⑧ ⑨ ⑩

EXERCISE / DAILY ACTIVITY

☐ Heck yes, I worked out.

☐ I managed to exercise a bit.

☐ No, I haven't exercised at all.

☐ I did some stuff, and that counts.

DETAILS

NOTES / TRIGGERS / IMPROVEMENTS

I AM GRATEFUL FOR...

Date: _____

How are you feeling today?

Like death	Terrible	Not good	Meh	Good	Great!	Amazing!

RATE YOUR PAIN LEVEL

(1) (2) (3) (4) (5) (6) (7) (8) (9) (10)

TODAY'S SYMPTOMS

☐ Fatigue   ☐ Insomnia   ☐ Malaise

☐ Joint pain   ☐ Anxiety   ☐ Depression

☐ Muscle weakness ☐ Muscle stiffness ☐ Muscle aches

☐ Headache   ☐ Brain fog   ☐ Forgetfulness

☐ _____   ☐ _____

☐ _____   ☐ _____

Other symptoms:

_____

_____

WHAT ABOUT YOUR...?   ## Feeling sick?

Mood   (1)(2)(3)(4)(5)(6)(7)(8)(9)(10)   ☐ Nope!

Energy levels   (1)(2)(3)(4)(5)(6)(7)(8)(9)(10)   ☐ Yes...

Mental clarity (1)(2)(3)(4)(5)(6)(7)(8)(9)(10)

☐ Nausea   ☐ Diarrhea   ☐ Vomiting   ☐ Sore throat

☐ Congestion ☐ Coughing   ☐ Chills   ☐ Fever

Other symptoms: _____

LAST NIGHT'S SLEEP

Hours of Sleep ① ② ③ ④ ⑤ ⑥ ⑦ ⑧ ⑨ ⑩ ⊕

Sleep Quality ① ② ③ ④ ⑤ ⑥ ⑦ ⑧ ⑨ ⑩

STRESS LEVELS

None	Low	Medium	High	Max	@$#%!

FOOD / MEDICATIONS

food / drinks	meds / supplements	time	dose

☐ usual daily medication

water ① ② ③ ④ ⑤ ⑥ ⑦ ⑧ ⑨ ⑩

caffeine ① ② ③ ④ ⑤ ⑥ ⑦ ⑧ ⑨ ⑩

alcohol ① ② ③ ④ ⑤ ⑥ ⑦ ⑧ ⑨ ⑩

EXERCISE / DAILY ACTIVITY

☐ Heck yes, I worked out.

☐ I managed to exercise a bit.

☐ No, I haven't exercised at all.

☐ I did some stuff, and that counts.

DETAILS

NOTES / TRIGGERS / IMPROVEMENTS

I AM GRATEFUL FOR...

Date: _____

How are you feeling today?

Like death   Terrible   Not good   Meh   Good   Great!   Amazing!

RATE YOUR PAIN LEVEL

(1) (2) (3) (4) (5) (6) (7) (8) (9) (10)

TODAY'S SYMPTOMS

☐ Fatigue   ☐ Insomnia   ☐ Malaise

☐ Joint pain   ☐ Anxiety   ☐ Depression

☐ Muscle weakness   ☐ Muscle stiffness ☐ Muscle aches

☐ Headache   ☐ Brain fog   ☐ Forgetfulness

☐ _____   ☐ _____

☐ _____   ☐ _____

Other symptoms:

_____

_____

WHAT ABOUT YOUR...?

Mood   ① ② ③ ④ ⑤ ⑥ ⑦ ⑧ ⑨ ⑩
Energy levels   ① ② ③ ④ ⑤ ⑥ ⑦ ⑧ ⑨ ⑩
Mental clarity   ① ② ③ ④ ⑤ ⑥ ⑦ ⑧ ⑨ ⑩

Feeling sick?

☐ Nope!
☐ Yes...

☐ Nausea   ☐ Diarrhea   ☐ Vomiting   ☐ Sore throat
☐ Congestion ☐ Coughing   ☐ Chills   ☐ Fever

Other symptoms: _____

LAST NIGHT'S SLEEP

Hours of Sleep ① ② ③ ④ ⑤ ⑥ ⑦ ⑧ ⑨ ⑩ ⊕

Sleep Quality ① ② ③ ④ ⑤ ⑥ ⑦ ⑧ ⑨ ⑩

STRESS LEVELS

None	Low	Medium	High	Max	@$#%!

FOOD / MEDICATIONS

food / drinks	meds / supplements	time	dose

☐ usual daily medication

water ⟹ ① ② ③ ④ ⑤ ⑥ ⑦ ⑧ ⑨ ⑩

caffeine ⟹ ① ② ③ ④ ⑤ ⑥ ⑦ ⑧ ⑨ ⑩

alcohol ⟹ ① ② ③ ④ ⑤ ⑥ ⑦ ⑧ ⑨ ⑩

EXERCISE / DAILY ACTIVITY

☐ Heck yes, I worked out.

☐ I managed to exercise a bit.

☐ No, I haven't exercised at all.

☐ I did some stuff, and that counts.

DETAILS

NOTES / TRIGGERS / IMPROVEMENTS

I AM GRATEFUL FOR...

Date:_____

How are you feeling today?

Like death	Terrible	Not good	Meh	Good	Great!	Amazing!

RATE YOUR PAIN LEVEL

(1) (2) (3) (4) (5) (6) (7) (8) (9) (10)

TODAY'S SYMPTOMS

☐ Fatigue   ☐ Insomnia   ☐ Malaise

☐ Joint pain   ☐ Anxiety   ☐ Depression

☐ Muscle weakness ☐ Muscle stiffness ☐ Muscle aches

☐ Headache   ☐ Brain fog   ☐ Forgetfulness

☐ _____   ☐ _____

☐ _____   ☐ _____

Other symptoms:

_____

_____

WHAT ABOUT YOUR...?   Feeling sick?

Mood	(1) (2) (3) (4) (5) (6) (7) (8) (9) (10)	☐ Nope!
Energy levels	(1) (2) (3) (4) (5) (6) (7) (8) (9) (10)	☐ Yes...
Mental clarity	(1) (2) (3) (4) (5) (6) (7) (8) (9) (10)	

☐ Nausea   ☐ Diarrhea   ☐ Vomiting   ☐ Sore throat

☐ Congestion   ☐ Coughing   ☐ Chills   ☐ Fever

Other symptoms: _____

LAST NIGHT'S SLEEP

Hours of Sleep (1) (2) (3) (4) (5) (6) (7) (8) (9) (10) (+)

Sleep Quality (1) (2) (3) (4) (5) (6) (7) (8) (9) (10)

STRESS LEVELS

None	Low	Medium	High	Max	@$#%!

FOOD / MEDICATIONS

food / drinks	meds / supplements	time	dose

☐ usual daily medication

water ⟹ (1) (2) (3) (4) (5) (6) (7) (8) (9) (10)

caffeine ⟹ (1) (2) (3) (4) (5) (6) (7) (8) (9) (10)

alcohol ⟹ (1) (2) (3) (4) (5) (6) (7) (8) (9) (10)

EXERCISE / DAILY ACTIVITY

☐ Heck yes, I worked out.

☐ I managed to exercise a bit.

☐ No, I haven't exercised at all.

☐ I did some stuff, and that counts.

DETAILS

NOTES / TRIGGERS / IMPROVEMENTS

I AM GRATEFUL FOR...

Date: _____

How are you feeling today?

Like death	Terrible	Not good	Meh	Good	Great!	Amazing!

RATE YOUR PAIN LEVEL

(1) (2) (3) (4) (5) (6) (7) (8) (9) (10)

TODAY'S SYMPTOMS

☐ Fatigue ☐ Insomnia ☐ Malaise

☐ Joint pain ☐ Anxiety ☐ Depression

☐ Muscle weakness ☐ Muscle stiffness ☐ Muscle aches

☐ Headache ☐ Brain fog ☐ Forgetfulness

☐ _____ ☐ _____

☐ _____ ☐ _____

Other symptoms:
_____
_____

WHAT ABOUT YOUR...?

		Feeling sick?
Mood	(1) (2) (3) (4) (5) (6) (7) (8) (9) (10)	☐ Nope!
Energy levels	(1) (2) (3) (4) (5) (6) (7) (8) (9) (10)	☐ Yes...
Mental clarity	(1) (2) (3) (4) (5) (6) (7) (8) (9) (10)	

☐ Nausea ☐ Diarrhea ☐ Vomiting ☐ Sore throat

☐ Congestion ☐ Coughing ☐ Chills ☐ Fever

Other symptoms: _____

LAST NIGHT'S SLEEP

Hours of Sleep ① ② ③ ④ ⑤ ⑥ ⑦ ⑧ ⑨ ⑩ ⊕

Sleep Quality ① ② ③ ④ ⑤ ⑥ ⑦ ⑧ ⑨ ⑩

STRESS LEVELS

None	Low	Medium	High	Max	@$#%!

FOOD / MEDICATIONS

food / drinks	meds / supplements	time	dose

☐ usual daily medication

water ⟹ ① ② ③ ④ ⑤ ⑥ ⑦ ⑧ ⑨ ⑩

caffeine ⟹ ① ② ③ ④ ⑤ ⑥ ⑦ ⑧ ⑨ ⑩

alcohol ⟹ ① ② ③ ④ ⑤ ⑥ ⑦ ⑧ ⑨ ⑩

EXERCISE / DAILY ACTIVITY

☐ Heck yes, I worked out.

☐ I managed to exercise a bit.

☐ No, I haven't exercised at all.

☐ I did some stuff, and that counts.

DETAILS

NOTES / TRIGGERS / IMPROVEMENTS

I AM GRATEFUL FOR...

Date:_____

How are you feeling today?

Like death   Terrible   Not good   Meh   Good   Great!   Amazing!

RATE YOUR PAIN LEVEL

(1) (2) (3) (4) (5) (6) (7) (8) (9) (10)

TODAY'S SYMPTOMS

☐ Fatigue   ☐ Insomnia   ☐ Malaise

☐ Joint pain   ☐ Anxiety   ☐ Depression

☐ Muscle weakness   ☐ Muscle stiffness   ☐ Muscle aches

☐ Headache   ☐ Brain fog   ☐ Forgetfulness

☐ _____   ☐ _____

☐ _____   ☐ _____

Other symptoms:

_____

_____

WHAT ABOUT YOUR...?

Mood   ① ② ③ ④ ⑤ ⑥ ⑦ ⑧ ⑨ ⑩

Energy levels   ① ② ③ ④ ⑤ ⑥ ⑦ ⑧ ⑨ ⑩

Mental clarity   ① ② ③ ④ ⑤ ⑥ ⑦ ⑧ ⑨ ⑩

Feeling sick?

☐ Nope!

☐ Yes...

☐ Nausea   ☐ Diarrhea   ☐ Vomiting   ☐ Sore throat

☐ Congestion   ☐ Coughing   ☐ Chills   ☐ Fever

Other symptoms: _____

LET'S EXPLORE SOME MORE #37

LAST NIGHT'S SLEEP

Hours of Sleep ① ② ③ ④ ⑤ ⑥ ⑦ ⑧ ⑨ ⑩ ⊕

Sleep Quality ① ② ③ ④ ⑤ ⑥ ⑦ ⑧ ⑨ ⑩

STRESS LEVELS

None	Low	Medium	High	Max	@$#%!

FOOD / MEDICATIONS

food / drinks	meds / supplements	time	dose

☐ usual daily medication

water ⟹ ① ② ③ ④ ⑤ ⑥ ⑦ ⑧ ⑨ ⑩

caffeine ⟹ ① ② ③ ④ ⑤ ⑥ ⑦ ⑧ ⑨ ⑩

alcohol ⟹ ① ② ③ ④ ⑤ ⑥ ⑦ ⑧ ⑨ ⑩

EXERCISE / DAILY ACTIVITY

☐ Heck yes, I worked out.

☐ I managed to exercise a bit.

☐ No, I haven't exercised at all.

☐ I did some stuff, and that counts.

DETAILS

NOTES / TRIGGERS / IMPROVEMENTS

I AM GRATEFUL FOR...

Date: _____

How are you feeling today?

Like death	Terrible	Not good	Meh	Good	Great!	Amazing!

RATE YOUR PAIN LEVEL

① ② ③ ④ ⑤ ⑥ ⑦ ⑧ ⑨ ⑩

TODAY'S SYMPTOMS

□ Fatigue   □ Insomnia   □ Malaise

□ Joint pain   □ Anxiety   □ Depression

□ Muscle weakness   □ Muscle stiffness   □ Muscle aches

□ Headache   □ Brain fog   □ Forgetfulness

□ _____   □ _____

□ _____   □ _____

Other symptoms:

_____

_____

WHAT ABOUT YOUR...?

Mood   ① ② ③ ④ ⑤ ⑥ ⑦ ⑧ ⑨ ⑩

Energy levels   ① ② ③ ④ ⑤ ⑥ ⑦ ⑧ ⑨ ⑩

Mental clarity   ① ② ③ ④ ⑤ ⑥ ⑦ ⑧ ⑨ ⑩

Feeling sick?

□ Nope!

□ Yes...

□ Nausea   □ Diarrhea   □ Vomiting   □ Sore throat

□ Congestion   □ Coughing   □ Chills   □ Fever

Other symptoms: _____

LAST NIGHT'S SLEEP

Hours of Sleep ① ② ③ ④ ⑤ ⑥ ⑦ ⑧ ⑨ ⑩ ⊕

Sleep Quality ① ② ③ ④ ⑤ ⑥ ⑦ ⑧ ⑨ ⑩

STRESS LEVELS

None	Low	Medium	High	Max	@$#%!

FOOD / MEDICATIONS

food / drinks	meds / supplements	time	dose

☐ usual daily medication

water ⟹ ① ② ③ ④ ⑤ ⑥ ⑦ ⑧ ⑨ ⑩

caffeine ⟹ ① ② ③ ④ ⑤ ⑥ ⑦ ⑧ ⑨ ⑩

alcohol ⟹ ① ② ③ ④ ⑤ ⑥ ⑦ ⑧ ⑨ ⑩

EXERCISE / DAILY ACTIVITY

☐ Heck yes, I worked out.

☐ I managed to exercise a bit.

☐ No, I haven't exercised at all.

☐ I did some stuff, and that counts.

NOTES / TRIGGERS / IMPROVEMENTS

DETAILS

I AM GRATEFUL FOR...

Date: _____

How are you feeling today?

Like death	Terrible	Not good	Meh	Good	Great!	Amazing!

RATE YOUR PAIN LEVEL

① ② ③ ④ ⑤ ⑥ ⑦ ⑧ ⑨ ⑩

TODAY'S SYMPTOMS

☐ Fatigue   ☐ Insomnia   ☐ Malaise

☐ Joint pain   ☐ Anxiety   ☐ Depression

☐ Muscle weakness ☐ Muscle stiffness ☐ Muscle aches

☐ Headache   ☐ Brain fog   ☐ Forgetfulness

☐ _____   ☐ _____

☐ _____   ☐ _____

Other symptoms:

_____

_____

WHAT ABOUT YOUR...?   **Feeling sick?**

Mood	① ② ③ ④ ⑤ ⑥ ⑦ ⑧ ⑨ ⑩	☐ Nope!
Energy levels	① ② ③ ④ ⑤ ⑥ ⑦ ⑧ ⑨ ⑩	☐ Yes...
Mental clarity	① ② ③ ④ ⑤ ⑥ ⑦ ⑧ ⑨ ⑩	

☐ Nausea   ☐ Diarrhea   ☐ Vomiting   ☐ Sore throat

☐ Congestion ☐ Coughing   ☐ Chills   ☐ Fever

Other symptoms: _____

LET'S EXPLORE SOME MORE

LAST NIGHT'S SLEEP

Hours of Sleep (1) (2) (3) (4) (5) (6) (7) (8) (9) (10) (+)

Sleep Quality (1) (2) (3) (4) (5) (6) (7) (8) (9) (10)

STRESS LEVELS

None	Low	Medium	High	Max	@$#%!

FOOD / MEDICATIONS

food / drinks	meds / supplements	time	dose

☐ usual daily medication

water ⟹ (1) (2) (3) (4) (5) (6) (7) (8) (9) (10)

caffeine ⟹ (1) (2) (3) (4) (5) (6) (7) (8) (9) (10)

alcohol ⟹ (1) (2) (3) (4) (5) (6) (7) (8) (9) (10)

EXERCISE / DAILY ACTIVITY

☐ Heck yes, I worked out.

☐ I managed to exercise a bit.

☐ No, I haven't exercised at all.

☐ I did some stuff, and that counts.

DETAILS

NOTES / TRIGGERS / IMPROVEMENTS

I AM GRATEFUL FOR...

Date:_____

How are you feeling today?

Like death	Terrible	Not good	Meh	Good	Great!	Amazing!

RATE YOUR PAIN LEVEL

(1) (2) (3) (4) (5) (6) (7) (8) (9) (10)

TODAY'S SYMPTOMS

☐ Fatigue   ☐ Insomnia   ☐ Malaise

☐ Joint pain   ☐ Anxiety   ☐ Depression

☐ Muscle weakness   ☐ Muscle stiffness   ☐ Muscle aches

☐ Headache   ☐ Brain fog   ☐ Forgetfulness

☐ _____   ☐ _____

☐ _____   ☐ _____

Other symptoms:

_____

_____

WHAT ABOUT YOUR...?   ## Feeling sick?

Mood   (1)(2)(3)(4)(5)(6)(7)(8)(9)(10)   ☐ Nope!
Energy levels (1)(2)(3)(4)(5)(6)(7)(8)(9)(10)   ☐ Yes...
Mental clarity (1)(2)(3)(4)(5)(6)(7)(8)(9)(10)

☐ Nausea   ☐ Diarrhea   ☐ Vomiting   ☐ Sore throat
☐ Congestion   ☐ Coughing   ☐ Chills   ☐ Fever

Other symptoms: _____

LET'S EXPLORE SOME MORE

LAST NIGHT'S SLEEP

Hours of Sleep ① ② ③ ④ ⑤ ⑥ ⑦ ⑧ ⑨ ⑩ (+)

Sleep Quality ① ② ③ ④ ⑤ ⑥ ⑦ ⑧ ⑨ ⑩

STRESS LEVELS

None	Low	Medium	High	Max	@$#%!

FOOD / MEDICATIONS

food / drinks	meds / supplements	time	dose

☐ usual daily medication

water ⟹ ① ② ③ ④ ⑤ ⑥ ⑦ ⑧ ⑨ ⑩

caffeine ⟹ ① ② ③ ④ ⑤ ⑥ ⑦ ⑧ ⑨ ⑩

alcohol ⟹ ① ② ③ ④ ⑤ ⑥ ⑦ ⑧ ⑨ ⑩

EXERCISE / DAILY ACTIVITY

☐ Heck yes, I worked out.

☐ I managed to exercise a bit.

☐ No, I haven't exercised at all.

☐ I did some stuff, and that counts.

DETAILS

NOTES / TRIGGERS / IMPROVEMENTS

I AM GRATEFUL FOR...

Date:_____

How are you feeling today?

Like death	Terrible	Not good	Meh	Good	Great!	Amazing!

RATE YOUR PAIN LEVEL

(1) (2) (3) (4) (5) (6) (7) (8) (9) (10)

TODAY'S SYMPTOMS

☐ Fatigue   ☐ Insomnia   ☐ Malaise

☐ Joint pain   ☐ Anxiety   ☐ Depression

☐ Muscle weakness   ☐ Muscle stiffness   ☐ Muscle aches

☐ Headache   ☐ Brain fog   ☐ Forgetfulness

☐ _____   ☐ _____

☐ _____   ☐ _____

Other symptoms:

_____

WHAT ABOUT YOUR...?

Mood   (1)(2)(3)(4)(5)(6)(7)(8)(9)(10)

Energy levels   (1)(2)(3)(4)(5)(6)(7)(8)(9)(10)

Mental clarity   (1)(2)(3)(4)(5)(6)(7)(8)(9)(10)

Feeling sick?

☐ Nope!

☐ Yes...

☐ Nausea   ☐ Diarrhea   ☐ Vomiting   ☐ Sore throat

☐ Congestion   ☐ Coughing   ☐ Chills   ☐ Fever

Other symptoms: _____

LET'S EXPLORE SOME MORE #41

LAST NIGHT'S SLEEP

Hours of Sleep (1) (2) (3) (4) (5) (6) (7) (8) (9) (10) (+)

Sleep Quality (1) (2) (3) (4) (5) (6) (7) (8) (9) (10)

STRESS LEVELS

None	Low	Medium	High	Max	@$#%!

FOOD / MEDICATIONS

food / drinks	meds / supplements	time	dose

☐ usual daily medication

water ⟹ (1) (2) (3) (4) (5) (6) (7) (8) (9) (10)

caffeine ⟹ (1) (2) (3) (4) (5) (6) (7) (8) (9) (10)

alcohol ⟹ (1) (2) (3) (4) (5) (6) (7) (8) (9) (10)

EXERCISE / DAILY ACTIVITY

☐ Heck yes, I worked out.

☐ I managed to exercise a bit.

☐ No, I haven't exercised at all.

☐ I did some stuff, and that counts.

DETAILS

NOTES / TRIGGERS / IMPROVEMENTS

I AM GRATEFUL FOR...

Date:_____

How are you feeling today?

Like death	Terrible	Not good	Meh	Good	Great!	Amazing!

RATE YOUR PAIN LEVEL

① ② ③ ④ ⑤ ⑥ ⑦ ⑧ ⑨ ⑩

TODAY'S SYMPTOMS

☐ Fatigue   ☐ Insomnia   ☐ Malaise

☐ Joint pain   ☐ Anxiety   ☐ Depression

☐ Muscle weakness   ☐ Muscle stiffness ☐ Muscle aches

☐ Headache   ☐ Brain fog   ☐ Forgetfulness

☐ _____   ☐ _____

☐ _____   ☐ _____

Other symptoms:

_____

_____

WHAT ABOUT YOUR...?   **Feeling sick?**

Mood   ① ② ③ ④ ⑤ ⑥ ⑦ ⑧ ⑨ ⑩   ☐   Nope!
Energy levels ① ② ③ ④ ⑤ ⑥ ⑦ ⑧ ⑨ ⑩   ☐   Yes...
Mental clarity ① ② ③ ④ ⑤ ⑥ ⑦ ⑧ ⑨ ⑩

☐ Nausea   ☐ Diarrhea   ☐ Vomiting   ☐ Sore throat
☐ Congestion   ☐ Coughing   ☐ Chills   ☐ Fever

Other symptoms: _____

LET'S EXPLORE SOME MORE #42

LAST NIGHT'S SLEEP

Hours of Sleep (1)(2)(3)(4)(5)(6)(7)(8)(9)(10)(+)

Sleep Quality (1)(2)(3)(4)(5)(6)(7)(8)(9)(10)

STRESS LEVELS

None	Low	Medium	High	Max	@$#%!

FOOD / MEDICATIONS

food / drinks	meds / supplements	time	dose

☐ usual daily medication

water ⟹ (1)(2)(3)(4)(5)(6)(7)(8)(9)(10)

caffeine ⟹ (1)(2)(3)(4)(5)(6)(7)(8)(9)(10)

alcohol ⟹ (1)(2)(3)(4)(5)(6)(7)(8)(9)(10)

EXERCISE / DAILY ACTIVITY

☐ Heck yes, I worked out.

☐ I managed to exercise a bit.

☐ No, I haven't exercised at all.

☐ I did some stuff, and that counts.

DETAILS

NOTES / TRIGGERS / IMPROVEMENTS

I AM GRATEFUL FOR...

Date: _____

How are you feeling today?

| Like death | Terrible | Not good | Meh | Good | Great! | Amazing! |

RATE YOUR PAIN LEVEL

(1) (2) (3) (4) (5) (6) (7) (8) (9) (10)

TODAY'S SYMPTOMS

☐ Fatigue   ☐ Insomnia   ☐ Malaise

☐ Joint pain   ☐ Anxiety   ☐ Depression

☐ Muscle weakness ☐ Muscle stiffness   ☐ Muscle aches

☐ Headache   ☐ Brain fog   ☐ Forgetfulness

☐ _____   ☐ _____

☐ _____   ☐ _____

Other symptoms:

_____

_____

WHAT ABOUT YOUR...?   **Feeling sick?**

Mood   (1) (2) (3) (4) (5) (6) (7) (8) (9) (10)   ☐ Nope!

Energy levels   (1) (2) (3) (4) (5) (6) (7) (8) (9) (10)   ☐ Yes...

Mental clarity (1) (2) (3) (4) (5) (6) (7) (8) (9) (10)

☐ Nausea   ☐ Diarrhea   ☐ Vomiting   ☐ Sore throat

☐ Congestion   ☐ Coughing   ☐ Chills   ☐ Fever

Other symptoms: _____

LET'S EXPLORE SOME MORE #43

LAST NIGHT'S SLEEP

Hours of Sleep ① ② ③ ④ ⑤ ⑥ ⑦ ⑧ ⑨ ⑩ ⊕

Sleep Quality ① ② ③ ④ ⑤ ⑥ ⑦ ⑧ ⑨ ⑩

STRESS LEVELS

None	Low	Medium	High	Max	@$#%!

FOOD / MEDICATIONS

food / drinks	meds / supplements	time	dose

☐ usual daily medication

water ① ② ③ ④ ⑤ ⑥ ⑦ ⑧ ⑨ ⑩
caffeine ① ② ③ ④ ⑤ ⑥ ⑦ ⑧ ⑨ ⑩
alcohol ① ② ③ ④ ⑤ ⑥ ⑦ ⑧ ⑨ ⑩

EXERCISE / DAILY ACTIVITY

☐ Heck yes, I worked out.
☐ I managed to exercise a bit.
☐ No, I haven't exercised at all.
☐ I did some stuff, and that counts.

DETAILS

NOTES / TRIGGERS / IMPROVEMENTS

I AM GRATEFUL FOR...

Date: _____

How are you feeling today?

| Like death | Terrible | Not good | Meh | Good | Great! | Amazing! |

RATE YOUR PAIN LEVEL

① ② ③ ④ ⑤ ⑥ ⑦ ⑧ ⑨ ⑩

TODAY'S SYMPTOMS

☐ Fatigue   ☐ Insomnia   ☐ Malaise

☐ Joint pain   ☐ Anxiety   ☐ Depression

☐ Muscle weakness   ☐ Muscle stiffness   ☐ Muscle aches

☐ Headache   ☐ Brain fog   ☐ Forgetfulness

☐ _____   ☐ _____

☐ _____   ☐ _____

Other symptoms:

_____

WHAT ABOUT YOUR...?   Feeling sick?

Mood	① ② ③ ④ ⑤ ⑥ ⑦ ⑧ ⑨ ⑩	☐ Nope!
Energy levels	① ② ③ ④ ⑤ ⑥ ⑦ ⑧ ⑨ ⑩	☐ Yes...
Mental clarity	① ② ③ ④ ⑤ ⑥ ⑦ ⑧ ⑨ ⑩	

☐ Nausea   ☐ Diarrhea   ☐ Vomiting   ☐ Sore throat

☐ Congestion   ☐ Coughing   ☐ Chills   ☐ Fever

Other symptoms: _____

LET'S EXPLORE SOME MORE #44

LAST NIGHT'S SLEEP

Hours of Sleep (1)(2)(3)(4)(5)(6)(7)(8)(9)(10)(+)

Sleep Quality (1)(2)(3)(4)(5)(6)(7)(8)(9)(10)

STRESS LEVELS

None	Low	Medium	High	Max	@$#%!

FOOD / MEDICATIONS

food / drinks	meds / supplements	time	dose

☐ usual daily medication

water → (1)(2)(3)(4)(5)(6)(7)(8)(9)(10)

caffeine → (1)(2)(3)(4)(5)(6)(7)(8)(9)(10)

alcohol → (1)(2)(3)(4)(5)(6)(7)(8)(9)(10)

EXERCISE / DAILY ACTIVITY

☐ Heck yes, I worked out.

☐ I managed to exercise a bit.

☐ No, I haven't exercised at all.

☐ I did some stuff, and that counts.

DETAILS

NOTES / TRIGGERS / IMPROVEMENTS

I AM GRATEFUL FOR...

Date:_____

How are you feeling today?

Like death	Terrible	Not good	Meh	Good	Great!	Amazing!

RATE YOUR PAIN LEVEL

① ② ③ ④ ⑤ ⑥ ⑦ ⑧ ⑨ ⑩

TODAY'S SYMPTOMS

☐ Fatigue   ☐ Insomnia   ☐ Malaise

☐ Joint pain   ☐ Anxiety   ☐ Depression

☐ Muscle weakness   ☐ Muscle stiffness   ☐ Muscle aches

☐ Headache   ☐ Brain fog   ☐ Forgetfulness

☐ _____   ☐ _____

☐ _____   ☐ _____

Other symptoms:

_____

WHAT ABOUT YOUR...?   ## Feeling sick?

Mood   ① ② ③ ④ ⑤ ⑥ ⑦ ⑧ ⑨ ⑩   ☐ Nope!

Energy levels   ① ② ③ ④ ⑤ ⑥ ⑦ ⑧ ⑨ ⑩   ☐ Yes...

Mental clarity ① ② ③ ④ ⑤ ⑥ ⑦ ⑧ ⑨ ⑩

☐ Nausea   ☐ Diarrhea   ☐ Vomiting   ☐ Sore throat

☐ Congestion   ☐ Coughing   ☐ Chills   ☐ Fever

Other symptoms: _____

LET'S EXPLORE SOME MORE

LAST NIGHT'S SLEEP

Hours of Sleep ① ② ③ ④ ⑤ ⑥ ⑦ ⑧ ⑨ ⑩ ⊕

Sleep Quality ① ② ③ ④ ⑤ ⑥ ⑦ ⑧ ⑨ ⑩

STRESS LEVELS

None	Low	Medium	High	Max	@$#%!

FOOD / MEDICATIONS

food / drinks	meds / supplements	time	dose

☐ usual daily medication

water ⟹ ① ② ③ ④ ⑤ ⑥ ⑦ ⑧ ⑨ ⑩

caffeine ⟹ ① ② ③ ④ ⑤ ⑥ ⑦ ⑧ ⑨ ⑩

alcohol ⟹ ① ② ③ ④ ⑤ ⑥ ⑦ ⑧ ⑨ ⑩

EXERCISE / DAILY ACTIVITY

☐ Heck yes, I worked out.

☐ I managed to exercise a bit.

☐ No, I haven't exercised at all.

☐ I did some stuff, and that counts.

DETAILS

NOTES / TRIGGERS / IMPROVEMENTS

I AM GRATEFUL FOR...

Date: _____

How are you feeling today?

Like death	Terrible	Not good	Meh	Good	Great!	Amazing!

RATE YOUR PAIN LEVEL

① ② ③ ④ ⑤ ⑥ ⑦ ⑧ ⑨ ⑩

TODAY'S SYMPTOMS

☐ Fatigue   ☐ Insomnia   ☐ Malaise

☐ Joint pain   ☐ Anxiety   ☐ Depression

☐ Muscle weakness   ☐ Muscle stiffness   ☐ Muscle aches

☐ Headache   ☐ Brain fog   ☐ Forgetfulness

☐ _____   ☐ _____

☐ _____   ☐ _____

Other symptoms:

_____

_____

WHAT ABOUT YOUR...?   **Feeling sick?**

Mood	① ② ③ ④ ⑤ ⑥ ⑦ ⑧ ⑨ ⑩	☐ Nope!
Energy levels	① ② ③ ④ ⑤ ⑥ ⑦ ⑧ ⑨ ⑩	☐ Yes...
Mental clarity	① ② ③ ④ ⑤ ⑥ ⑦ ⑧ ⑨ ⑩	

☐ Nausea   ☐ Diarrhea   ☐ Vomiting   ☐ Sore throat

☐ Congestion ☐ Coughing   ☐ Chills   ☐ Fever

Other symptoms: _____

LET'S EXPLORE SOME MORE #46

LAST NIGHT'S SLEEP

Hours of Sleep (1) (2) (3) (4) (5) (6) (7) (8) (9) (10) (+)

Sleep Quality (1) (2) (3) (4) (5) (6) (7) (8) (9) (10)

STRESS LEVELS

None	Low	Medium	High	Max	@$#%!

FOOD / MEDICATIONS

food / drinks	meds / supplements	time	dose

☐ usual daily medication

water ⟹ (1) (2) (3) (4) (5) (6) (7) (8) (9) (10)

caffeine ⟹ (1) (2) (3) (4) (5) (6) (7) (8) (9) (10)

alcohol ⟹ (1) (2) (3) (4) (5) (6) (7) (8) (9) (10)

EXERCISE / DAILY ACTIVITY

☐ Heck yes, I worked out.

☐ I managed to exercise a bit.

☐ No, I haven't exercised at all.

☐ I did some stuff, and that counts.

DETAILS

NOTES / TRIGGERS / IMPROVEMENTS

I AM GRATEFUL FOR...

Date: _____

How are you feeling today?

Like death	Terrible	Not good	Meh	Good	Great!	Amazing!

RATE YOUR PAIN LEVEL

(1) (2) (3) (4) (5) (6) (7) (8) (9) (10)

TODAY'S SYMPTOMS

☐ Fatigue   ☐ Insomnia   ☐ Malaise

☐ Joint pain   ☐ Anxiety   ☐ Depression

☐ Muscle weakness ☐ Muscle stiffness ☐ Muscle aches

☐ Headache   ☐ Brain fog   ☐ Forgetfulness

☐ _____   ☐ _____

☐ _____   ☐ _____

Other symptoms:

_____

_____

WHAT ABOUT YOUR...?   **Feeling sick?**

Mood	(1)(2)(3)(4)(5)(6)(7)(8)(9)(10)	☐ Nope!
Energy levels	(1)(2)(3)(4)(5)(6)(7)(8)(9)(10)	☐ Yes...
Mental clarity	(1)(2)(3)(4)(5)(6)(7)(8)(9)(10)	

☐ Nausea   ☐ Diarrhea   ☐ Vomiting   ☐ Sore throat

☐ Congestion ☐ Coughing   ☐ Chills   ☐ Fever

Other symptoms: _____

LET'S EXPLORE SOME MORE #47

LAST NIGHT'S SLEEP

Hours of Sleep ① ② ③ ④ ⑤ ⑥ ⑦ ⑧ ⑨ ⑩ ⊕

Sleep Quality ① ② ③ ④ ⑤ ⑥ ⑦ ⑧ ⑨ ⑩

STRESS LEVELS

None	Low	Medium	High	Max	@$#%!

FOOD / MEDICATIONS

food / drinks	meds / supplements	time	dose

☐ usual daily medication

water ⟹ ① ② ③ ④ ⑤ ⑥ ⑦ ⑧ ⑨ ⑩

caffeine ⟹ ① ② ③ ④ ⑤ ⑥ ⑦ ⑧ ⑨ ⑩

alcohol ⟹ ① ② ③ ④ ⑤ ⑥ ⑦ ⑧ ⑨ ⑩

EXERCISE / DAILY ACTIVITY

☐ Heck yes, I worked out.

☐ I managed to exercise a bit.

☐ No, I haven't exercised at all.

☐ I did some stuff, and that counts.

DETAILS

NOTES / TRIGGERS / IMPROVEMENTS

I AM GRATEFUL FOR...

Date: _____

How are you feeling today?

Like death	Terrible	Not good	Meh	Good	Great!	Amazing!

RATE YOUR PAIN LEVEL

(1) (2) (3) (4) (5) (6) (7) (8) (9) (10)

TODAY'S SYMPTOMS

☐ Fatigue ☐ Insomnia ☐ Malaise

☐ Joint pain ☐ Anxiety ☐ Depression

☐ Muscle weakness ☐ Muscle stiffness ☐ Muscle aches

☐ Headache ☐ Brain fog ☐ Forgetfulness

☐ _____ ☐ _____

☐ _____ ☐ _____

Other symptoms:

_____

_____

WHAT ABOUT YOUR...?   ## Feeling sick?

Mood   (1)(2)(3)(4)(5)(6)(7)(8)(9)(10)   ☐ Nope!

Energy levels (1)(2)(3)(4)(5)(6)(7)(8)(9)(10)   ☐ Yes...

Mental clarity (1)(2)(3)(4)(5)(6)(7)(8)(9)(10)

☐ Nausea ☐ Diarrhea ☐ Vomiting ☐ Sore throat

☐ Congestion ☐ Coughing ☐ Chills ☐ Fever

Other symptoms: _____

LAST NIGHT'S SLEEP

Hours of Sleep   ① ② ③ ④ ⑤ ⑥ ⑦ ⑧ ⑨ ⑩ ⊕

Sleep Quality   ① ② ③ ④ ⑤ ⑥ ⑦ ⑧ ⑨ ⑩

STRESS LEVELS

None	Low	Medium	High	Max	@$#%!

FOOD / MEDICATIONS

food / drinks	meds / supplements	time	dose

☐ usual daily medication

water	⟹	① ② ③ ④ ⑤ ⑥ ⑦ ⑧ ⑨ ⑩
caffeine	⟹	① ② ③ ④ ⑤ ⑥ ⑦ ⑧ ⑨ ⑩
alcohol	⟹	① ② ③ ④ ⑤ ⑥ ⑦ ⑧ ⑨ ⑩

EXERCISE / DAILY ACTIVITY

☐ Heck yes, I worked out.

☐ I managed to exercise a bit.

☐ No, I haven't exercised at all.

☐ I did some stuff, and that counts.

NOTES / TRIGGERS / IMPROVEMENTS

DETAILS

I AM GRATEFUL FOR…

Date: _____

How are you feeling today?

| Like death | Terrible | Not good | Meh | Good | Great! | Amazing! |

RATE YOUR PAIN LEVEL

(1) (2) (3) (4) (5) (6) (7) (8) (9) (10)

TODAY'S SYMPTOMS

☐ Fatigue   ☐ Insomnia   ☐ Malaise

☐ Joint pain   ☐ Anxiety   ☐ Depression

☐ Muscle weakness   ☐ Muscle stiffness   ☐ Muscle aches

☐ Headache   ☐ Brain fog   ☐ Forgetfulness

☐ _____   ☐ _____

☐ _____   ☐ _____

Other symptoms:

_____

_____

WHAT ABOUT YOUR...?   Feeling sick?

Mood   (1) (2) (3) (4) (5) (6) (7) (8) (9) (10)   ☐   Nope!

Energy levels   (1) (2) (3) (4) (5) (6) (7) (8) (9) (10)   ☐   Yes...

Mental clarity   (1) (2) (3) (4) (5) (6) (7) (8) (9) (10)

☐ Nausea   ☐ Diarrhea   ☐ Vomiting   ☐ Sore throat

☐ Congestion   ☐ Coughing   ☐ Chills   ☐ Fever

Other symptoms: _____

LAST NIGHT'S SLEEP

Hours of Sleep (1) (2) (3) (4) (5) (6) (7) (8) (9) (10) (+)

Sleep Quality (1) (2) (3) (4) (5) (6) (7) (8) (9) (10)

STRESS LEVELS

None	Low	Medium	High	Max	@$#%!

FOOD / MEDICATIONS

food / drinks	meds / supplements	time	dose

☐ usual daily medication

water ⟹ (1) (2) (3) (4) (5) (6) (7) (8) (9) (10)

caffeine ⟹ (1) (2) (3) (4) (5) (6) (7) (8) (9) (10)

alcohol ⟹ (1) (2) (3) (4) (5) (6) (7) (8) (9) (10)

EXERCISE / DAILY ACTIVITY

☐ Heck yes, I worked out.

☐ I managed to exercise a bit.

☐ No, I haven't exercised at all.

☐ I did some stuff, and that counts.

DETAILS

NOTES / TRIGGERS / IMPROVEMENTS

I AM GRATEFUL FOR...

Date: _____

How are you feeling today?

Like death	Terrible	Not good	Meh	Good	Great!	Amazing!

RATE YOUR PAIN LEVEL

① ② ③ ④ ⑤ ⑥ ⑦ ⑧ ⑨ ⑩

TODAY'S SYMPTOMS

☐ Fatigue ☐ Insomnia ☐ Malaise

☐ Joint pain ☐ Anxiety ☐ Depression

☐ Muscle weakness ☐ Muscle stiffness ☐ Muscle aches

☐ Headache ☐ Brain fog ☐ Forgetfulness

☐ _____ ☐ _____

☐ _____ ☐ _____

Other symptoms:

_____

WHAT ABOUT YOUR...?

Feeling sick?

Mood ① ② ③ ④ ⑤ ⑥ ⑦ ⑧ ⑨ ⑩ ☐ Nope!

Energy levels ① ② ③ ④ ⑤ ⑥ ⑦ ⑧ ⑨ ⑩ ☐ Yes...

Mental clarity ① ② ③ ④ ⑤ ⑥ ⑦ ⑧ ⑨ ⑩

☐ Nausea ☐ Diarrhea ☐ Vomiting ☐ Sore throat
☐ Congestion ☐ Coughing ☐ Chills ☐ Fever

Other symptoms: _____

LET'S EXPLORE SOME MORE #50

LAST NIGHT'S SLEEP

Hours of Sleep ① ② ③ ④ ⑤ ⑥ ⑦ ⑧ ⑨ ⑩ ⊕

Sleep Quality ① ② ③ ④ ⑤ ⑥ ⑦ ⑧ ⑨ ⑩

STRESS LEVELS

None	Low	Medium	High	Max	@$#%!

FOOD / MEDICATIONS

food / drinks	meds / supplements	time	dose

☐ usual daily medication

water ⟹ ① ② ③ ④ ⑤ ⑥ ⑦ ⑧ ⑨ ⑩

caffeine ⟹ ① ② ③ ④ ⑤ ⑥ ⑦ ⑧ ⑨ ⑩

alcohol ⟹ ① ② ③ ④ ⑤ ⑥ ⑦ ⑧ ⑨ ⑩

EXERCISE / DAILY ACTIVITY

☐ Heck yes, I worked out.

☐ I managed to exercise a bit.

☐ No, I haven't exercised at all.

☐ I did some stuff, and that counts.

DETAILS

NOTES / TRIGGERS / IMPROVEMENTS

I AM GRATEFUL FOR...

Date: _____

How are you feeling today?

Like death	Terrible	Not good	Meh	Good	Great!	Amazing!

RATE YOUR PAIN LEVEL

(1) (2) (3) (4) (5) (6) (7) (8) (9) (10)

TODAY'S SYMPTOMS

☐ Fatigue   ☐ Insomnia   ☐ Malaise

☐ Joint pain   ☐ Anxiety   ☐ Depression

☐ Muscle weakness ☐ Muscle stiffness ☐ Muscle aches

☐ Headache   ☐ Brain fog   ☐ Forgetfulness

☐ _____   ☐ _____

☐ _____   ☐ _____

Other symptoms:

_____

_____

WHAT ABOUT YOUR...?   ### Feeling sick?

Mood   (1)(2)(3)(4)(5)(6)(7)(8)(9)(10)   ☐ Nope!

Energy levels (1)(2)(3)(4)(5)(6)(7)(8)(9)(10)   ☐ Yes...

Mental clarity (1)(2)(3)(4)(5)(6)(7)(8)(9)(10)

☐ Nausea   ☐ Diarrhea   ☐ Vomiting   ☐ Sore throat

☐ Congestion   ☐ Coughing   ☐ Chills   ☐ Fever

Other symptoms: _____

LAST NIGHT'S SLEEP

Hours of Sleep ① ② ③ ④ ⑤ ⑥ ⑦ ⑧ ⑨ ⑩ ⊕

Sleep Quality ① ② ③ ④ ⑤ ⑥ ⑦ ⑧ ⑨ ⑩

STRESS LEVELS

None	Low	Medium	High	Max	@$#%!

FOOD / MEDICATIONS

food / drinks	meds / supplements	time	dose

☐ usual daily medication

water ① ② ③ ④ ⑤ ⑥ ⑦ ⑧ ⑨ ⑩

caffeine ① ② ③ ④ ⑤ ⑥ ⑦ ⑧ ⑨ ⑩

alcohol ① ② ③ ④ ⑤ ⑥ ⑦ ⑧ ⑨ ⑩

EXERCISE / DAILY ACTIVITY

☐ Heck yes, I worked out.

☐ I managed to exercise a bit.

☐ No, I haven't exercised at all.

☐ I did some stuff, and that counts.

DETAILS

NOTES / TRIGGERS / IMPROVEMENTS

I AM GRATEFUL FOR...

Date:_____

How are you feeling today?

| Like death | Terrible | Not good | Meh | Good | Great! | Amazing! |

RATE YOUR PAIN LEVEL

① ② ③ ④ ⑤ ⑥ ⑦ ⑧ ⑨ ⑩

TODAY'S SYMPTOMS

☐ Fatigue   ☐ Insomnia   ☐ Malaise

☐ Joint pain   ☐ Anxiety   ☐ Depression

☐ Muscle weakness ☐ Muscle stiffness ☐ Muscle aches

☐ Headache   ☐ Brain fog   ☐ Forgetfulness

☐ _____   ☐ _____

☐ _____   ☐ _____

Other symptoms:
_____
_____

WHAT ABOUT YOUR...?

Mood   ① ② ③ ④ ⑤ ⑥ ⑦ ⑧ ⑨ ⑩
Energy levels   ① ② ③ ④ ⑤ ⑥ ⑦ ⑧ ⑨ ⑩
Mental clarity ① ② ③ ④ ⑤ ⑥ ⑦ ⑧ ⑨ ⑩

Feeling sick?

☐ Nope!
☐ Yes...

☐ Nausea   ☐ Diarrhea   ☐ Vomiting   ☐ Sore throat
☐ Congestion ☐ Coughing   ☐ Chills   ☐ Fever

Other symptoms: _____

LAST NIGHT'S SLEEP

Hours of Sleep (1) (2) (3) (4) (5) (6) (7) (8) (9) (10) (+)

Sleep Quality (1) (2) (3) (4) (5) (6) (7) (8) (9) (10)

STRESS LEVELS

None	Low	Medium	High	Max	@$#%!

FOOD / MEDICATIONS

food / drinks	meds / supplements	time	dose

☐ usual daily medication

water → (1) (2) (3) (4) (5) (6) (7) (8) (9) (10)

caffeine → (1) (2) (3) (4) (5) (6) (7) (8) (9) (10)

alcohol → (1) (2) (3) (4) (5) (6) (7) (8) (9) (10)

EXERCISE / DAILY ACTIVITY

☐ Heck yes, I worked out.

☐ I managed to exercise a bit.

☐ No, I haven't exercised at all.

☐ I did some stuff, and that counts.

DETAILS

NOTES / TRIGGERS / IMPROVEMENTS

I AM GRATEFUL FOR...

Date: _____

How are you feeling today?

Like death   Terrible   Not good   Meh   Good   Great!   Amazing!

RATE YOUR PAIN LEVEL

① ② ③ ④ ⑤ ⑥ ⑦ ⑧ ⑨ ⑩

TODAY'S SYMPTOMS

☐ Fatigue   ☐ Insomnia   ☐ Malaise

☐ Joint pain   ☐ Anxiety   ☐ Depression

☐ Muscle weakness   ☐ Muscle stiffness   ☐ Muscle aches

☐ Headache   ☐ Brain fog   ☐ Forgetfulness

☐ _____   ☐ _____

☐ _____   ☐ _____

Other symptoms:

_____

_____

WHAT ABOUT YOUR...?   **Feeling sick?**

Mood   ① ② ③ ④ ⑤ ⑥ ⑦ ⑧ ⑨ ⑩   ☐   Nope!

Energy levels   ① ② ③ ④ ⑤ ⑥ ⑦ ⑧ ⑨ ⑩   ☐   Yes...

Mental clarity ① ② ③ ④ ⑤ ⑥ ⑦ ⑧ ⑨ ⑩

☐ Nausea   ☐ Diarrhea   ☐ Vomiting   ☐ Sore throat

☐ Congestion   ☐ Coughing   ☐ Chills   ☐ Fever

Other symptoms: _____

LAST NIGHT'S SLEEP

Hours of Sleep ① ② ③ ④ ⑤ ⑥ ⑦ ⑧ ⑨ ⑩ ⊕

Sleep Quality ① ② ③ ④ ⑤ ⑥ ⑦ ⑧ ⑨ ⑩

STRESS LEVELS

None	Low	Medium	High	Max	@$#%!

FOOD / MEDICATIONS

food / drinks	meds / supplements	time	dose

☐ usual daily medication

water ⟹ ① ② ③ ④ ⑤ ⑥ ⑦ ⑧ ⑨ ⑩

caffeine ⟹ ① ② ③ ④ ⑤ ⑥ ⑦ ⑧ ⑨ ⑩

alcohol ⟹ ① ② ③ ④ ⑤ ⑥ ⑦ ⑧ ⑨ ⑩

EXERCISE / DAILY ACTIVITY

☐ Heck yes, I worked out.

☐ I managed to exercise a bit.

☐ No, I haven't exercised at all.

☐ I did some stuff, and that counts.

DETAILS

NOTES / TRIGGERS / IMPROVEMENTS

I AM GRATEFUL FOR...

Date: _____

How are you feeling today?

| Like death | Terrible | Not good | Meh | Good | Great! | Amazing! |

RATE YOUR PAIN LEVEL

(1) (2) (3) (4) (5) (6) (7) (8) (9) (10)

TODAY'S SYMPTOMS

☐ Fatigue   ☐ Insomnia   ☐ Malaise

☐ Joint pain   ☐ Anxiety   ☐ Depression

☐ Muscle weakness   ☐ Muscle stiffness   ☐ Muscle aches

☐ Headache   ☐ Brain fog   ☐ Forgetfulness

☐ _____   ☐ _____

☐ _____   ☐ _____

Other symptoms:

_____

WHAT ABOUT YOUR...?

Feeling sick?

Mood	(1) (2) (3) (4) (5) (6) (7) (8) (9) (10)	☐ Nope!
Energy levels	(1) (2) (3) (4) (5) (6) (7) (8) (9) (10)	☐ Yes...
Mental clarity	(1) (2) (3) (4) (5) (6) (7) (8) (9) (10)	

☐ Nausea   ☐ Diarrhea   ☐ Vomiting   ☐ Sore throat

☐ Congestion   ☐ Coughing   ☐ Chills   ☐ Fever

Other symptoms: _____

LET'S EXPLORE SOME MORE #54

LAST NIGHT'S SLEEP

Hours of Sleep ① ② ③ ④ ⑤ ⑥ ⑦ ⑧ ⑨ ⑩ ⊕

Sleep Quality ① ② ③ ④ ⑤ ⑥ ⑦ ⑧ ⑨ ⑩

STRESS LEVELS

None	Low	Medium	High	Max	@$#%!

FOOD / MEDICATIONS

food / drinks	meds / supplements	time	dose

☐ usual daily medication

water ① ② ③ ④ ⑤ ⑥ ⑦ ⑧ ⑨ ⑩

caffeine ① ② ③ ④ ⑤ ⑥ ⑦ ⑧ ⑨ ⑩

alcohol ① ② ③ ④ ⑤ ⑥ ⑦ ⑧ ⑨ ⑩

EXERCISE / DAILY ACTIVITY

☐ Heck yes, I worked out.

☐ I managed to exercise a bit.

☐ No, I haven't exercised at all.

☐ I did some stuff, and that counts.

DETAILS

NOTES / TRIGGERS / IMPROVEMENTS

I AM GRATEFUL FOR...

Date: _____

How are you feeling today?

| Like death | Terrible | Not good | Meh | Good | Great! | Amazing! |

RATE YOUR PAIN LEVEL

(1) (2) (3) (4) (5) (6) (7) (8) (9) (10)

TODAY'S SYMPTOMS

☐ Fatigue ☐ Insomnia ☐ Malaise

☐ Joint pain ☐ Anxiety ☐ Depression

☐ Muscle weakness ☐ Muscle stiffness ☐ Muscle aches

☐ Headache ☐ Brain fog ☐ Forgetfulness

☐ _____ ☐ _____

☐ _____ ☐ _____

Other symptoms: _____

_____

WHAT ABOUT YOUR...?

Feeling sick?

Mood (1)(2)(3)(4)(5)(6)(7)(8)(9)(10) ☐ Nope!

Energy levels (1)(2)(3)(4)(5)(6)(7)(8)(9)(10) ☐ Yes...

Mental clarity (1)(2)(3)(4)(5)(6)(7)(8)(9)(10)

☐ Nausea ☐ Diarrhea ☐ Vomiting ☐ Sore throat

☐ Congestion ☐ Coughing ☐ Chills ☐ Fever

Other symptoms: _____

LET'S EXPLORE SOME MORE #55

LAST NIGHT'S SLEEP

Hours of Sleep   ① ② ③ ④ ⑤ ⑥ ⑦ ⑧ ⑨ ⑩ ⊕

Sleep Quality   ① ② ③ ④ ⑤ ⑥ ⑦ ⑧ ⑨ ⑩

STRESS LEVELS

None	Low	Medium	High	Max	@$#%!

FOOD / MEDICATIONS

food / drinks	meds / supplements	time	dose

☐ usual daily medication

water ⟹ ① ② ③ ④ ⑤ ⑥ ⑦ ⑧ ⑨ ⑩

caffeine ⟹ ① ② ③ ④ ⑤ ⑥ ⑦ ⑧ ⑨ ⑩

alcohol ⟹ ① ② ③ ④ ⑤ ⑥ ⑦ ⑧ ⑨ ⑩

EXERCISE / DAILY ACTIVITY

☐ Heck yes, I worked out.

☐ I managed to exercise a bit.

☐ No, I haven't exercised at all.

☐ I did some stuff, and that counts.

DETAILS

NOTES / TRIGGERS / IMPROVEMENTS

I AM GRATEFUL FOR...

Date: _____

How are you feeling today?

Like death	Terrible	Not good	Meh	Good	Great!	Amazing!

RATE YOUR PAIN LEVEL

① ② ③ ④ ⑤ ⑥ ⑦ ⑧ ⑨ ⑩

TODAY'S SYMPTOMS

☐ Fatigue   ☐ Insomnia   ☐ Malaise

☐ Joint pain   ☐ Anxiety   ☐ Depression

☐ Muscle weakness   ☐ Muscle stiffness   ☐ Muscle aches

☐ Headache   ☐ Brain fog   ☐ Forgetfulness

☐ _____   ☐ _____

☐ _____   ☐ _____

Other symptoms:

WHAT ABOUT YOUR...?   Feeling sick?

Mood   ① ② ③ ④ ⑤ ⑥ ⑦ ⑧ ⑨ ⑩   ☐ Nope!

Energy levels   ① ② ③ ④ ⑤ ⑥ ⑦ ⑧ ⑨ ⑩   ☐ Yes...

Mental clarity   ① ② ③ ④ ⑤ ⑥ ⑦ ⑧ ⑨ ⑩

☐ Nausea   ☐ Diarrhea   ☐ Vomiting   ☐ Sore throat

☐ Congestion   ☐ Coughing   ☐ Chills   ☐ Fever

Other symptoms: _____

LAST NIGHT'S SLEEP

Hours of Sleep (1) (2) (3) (4) (5) (6) (7) (8) (9) (10) (+)

Sleep Quality (1) (2) (3) (4) (5) (6) (7) (8) (9) (10)

STRESS LEVELS

None	Low	Medium	High	Max	@$#%!

FOOD / MEDICATIONS

food / drinks	meds / supplements	time	dose

☐ usual daily medication

water → (1) (2) (3) (4) (5) (6) (7) (8) (9) (10)

caffeine → (1) (2) (3) (4) (5) (6) (7) (8) (9) (10)

alcohol → (1) (2) (3) (4) (5) (6) (7) (8) (9) (10)

EXERCISE / DAILY ACTIVITY

☐ Heck yes, I worked out.

☐ I managed to exercise a bit.

☐ No, I haven't exercised at all.

☐ I did some stuff, and that counts.

DETAILS

NOTES / TRIGGERS / IMPROVEMENTS

I AM GRATEFUL FOR...

Date: _____

How are you feeling today?

| Like death | Terrible | Not good | Meh | Good | Great! | Amazing! |

RATE YOUR PAIN LEVEL

① ② ③ ④ ⑤ ⑥ ⑦ ⑧ ⑨ ⑩

TODAY'S SYMPTOMS

☐ Fatigue ☐ Insomnia ☐ Malaise

☐ Joint pain ☐ Anxiety ☐ Depression

☐ Muscle weakness ☐ Muscle stiffness ☐ Muscle aches

☐ Headache ☐ Brain fog ☐ Forgetfulness

☐ _____ ☐ _____

☐ _____ ☐ _____

Other symptoms:

_____

_____

WHAT ABOUT YOUR...?

Feeling sick?

Mood ① ② ③ ④ ⑤ ⑥ ⑦ ⑧ ⑨ ⑩ ☐ Nope!

Energy levels ① ② ③ ④ ⑤ ⑥ ⑦ ⑧ ⑨ ⑩ ☐ Yes...

Mental clarity ① ② ③ ④ ⑤ ⑥ ⑦ ⑧ ⑨ ⑩

☐ Nausea ☐ Diarrhea ☐ Vomiting ☐ Sore throat

☐ Congestion ☐ Coughing ☐ Chills ☐ Fever

Other symptoms: _____

LET'S EXPLORE SOME MORE #57

LAST NIGHT'S SLEEP

Hours of Sleep (1)(2)(3)(4)(5)(6)(7)(8)(9)(10)(+)

Sleep Quality (1)(2)(3)(4)(5)(6)(7)(8)(9)(10)

STRESS LEVELS

None	Low	Medium	High	Max	@$#%!

FOOD / MEDICATIONS

food / drinks	meds / supplements	time	dose

☐ usual daily medication

water → (1)(2)(3)(4)(5)(6)(7)(8)(9)(10)
caffeine → (1)(2)(3)(4)(5)(6)(7)(8)(9)(10)
alcohol → (1)(2)(3)(4)(5)(6)(7)(8)(9)(10)

EXERCISE / DAILY ACTIVITY

☐ Heck yes, I worked out.
☐ I managed to exercise a bit.
☐ No, I haven't exercised at all.
☐ I did some stuff, and that counts.

DETAILS

NOTES / TRIGGERS / IMPROVEMENTS

I AM GRATEFUL FOR…

Date:_____

How are you feeling today?

Like death	Terrible	Not good	Meh	Good	Great!	Amazing!

RATE YOUR PAIN LEVEL

(1) (2) (3) (4) (5) (6) (7) (8) (9) (10)

TODAY'S SYMPTOMS

☐ Fatigue   ☐ Insomnia   ☐ Malaise

☐ Joint pain   ☐ Anxiety   ☐ Depression

☐ Muscle weakness   ☐ Muscle stiffness   ☐ Muscle aches

☐ Headache   ☐ Brain fog   ☐ Forgetfulness

☐ _____   ☐ _____

☐ _____   ☐ _____

Other symptoms:

_____

_____

WHAT ABOUT YOUR...?

Mood   (1) (2) (3) (4) (5) (6) (7) (8) (9) (10)

Energy levels   (1) (2) (3) (4) (5) (6) (7) (8) (9) (10)

Mental clarity   (1) (2) (3) (4) (5) (6) (7) (8) (9) (10)

Feeling sick?

☐ Nope!

☐ Yes...

☐ Nausea   ☐ Diarrhea   ☐ Vomiting   ☐ Sore throat

☐ Congestion   ☐ Coughing   ☐ Chills   ☐ Fever

Other symptoms: _____

LAST NIGHT'S SLEEP

Hours of Sleep ① ② ③ ④ ⑤ ⑥ ⑦ ⑧ ⑨ ⑩ ⊕

Sleep Quality ① ② ③ ④ ⑤ ⑥ ⑦ ⑧ ⑨ ⑩

STRESS LEVELS

None	Low	Medium	High	Max	@$#%!

FOOD / MEDICATIONS

food / drinks	meds / supplements	time	dose

☐ usual daily medication

water ⟹ ① ② ③ ④ ⑤ ⑥ ⑦ ⑧ ⑨ ⑩

caffeine ⟹ ① ② ③ ④ ⑤ ⑥ ⑦ ⑧ ⑨ ⑩

alcohol ⟹ ① ② ③ ④ ⑤ ⑥ ⑦ ⑧ ⑨ ⑩

EXERCISE / DAILY ACTIVITY

☐ Heck yes, I worked out.

☐ I managed to exercise a bit.

☐ No, I haven't exercised at all.

☐ I did some stuff, and that counts.

DETAILS

NOTES / TRIGGERS / IMPROVEMENTS

I AM GRATEFUL FOR…

Date:_____

How are you feeling today?

Like death	Terrible	Not good	Meh	Good	Great!	Amazing!

RATE YOUR PAIN LEVEL

① ② ③ ④ ⑤ ⑥ ⑦ ⑧ ⑨ ⑩

TODAY'S SYMPTOMS

☐ Fatigue   ☐ Insomnia   ☐ Malaise

☐ Joint pain   ☐ Anxiety   ☐ Depression

☐ Muscle weakness   ☐ Muscle stiffness   ☐ Muscle aches

☐ Headache   ☐ Brain fog   ☐ Forgetfulness

☐ _____   ☐ _____

☐ _____   ☐ _____

Other symptoms:

WHAT ABOUT YOUR...?

Mood   ① ② ③ ④ ⑤ ⑥ ⑦ ⑧ ⑨ ⑩

Energy levels   ① ② ③ ④ ⑤ ⑥ ⑦ ⑧ ⑨ ⑩

Mental clarity   ① ② ③ ④ ⑤ ⑥ ⑦ ⑧ ⑨ ⑩

Feeling sick?

☐ Nope!

☐ Yes...

☐ Nausea   ☐ Diarrhea   ☐ Vomiting   ☐ Sore throat

☐ Congestion   ☐ Coughing   ☐ Chills   ☐ Fever

Other symptoms: _____

LAST NIGHT'S SLEEP

Hours of Sleep ① ② ③ ④ ⑤ ⑥ ⑦ ⑧ ⑨ ⑩ ⊕

Sleep Quality ① ② ③ ④ ⑤ ⑥ ⑦ ⑧ ⑨ ⑩

STRESS LEVELS

None	Low	Medium	High	Max	@$#%!

FOOD / MEDICATIONS

food / drinks	meds / supplements	time	dose

☐ usual daily medication

water ① ② ③ ④ ⑤ ⑥ ⑦ ⑧ ⑨ ⑩

caffeine ① ② ③ ④ ⑤ ⑥ ⑦ ⑧ ⑨ ⑩

alcohol ① ② ③ ④ ⑤ ⑥ ⑦ ⑧ ⑨ ⑩

EXERCISE / DAILY ACTIVITY

☐ Heck yes, I worked out.

☐ I managed to exercise a bit.

☐ No, I haven't exercised at all.

☐ I did some stuff, and that counts.

DETAILS

NOTES / TRIGGERS / IMPROVEMENTS

I AM GRATEFUL FOR...

Date: _____

How are you feeling today?

Like death   Terrible   Not good   Meh   Good   Great!   Amazing!

RATE YOUR PAIN LEVEL

① ② ③ ④ ⑤ ⑥ ⑦ ⑧ ⑨ ⑩

TODAY'S SYMPTOMS

☐ Fatigue   ☐ Insomnia   ☐ Malaise

☐ Joint pain   ☐ Anxiety   ☐ Depression

☐ Muscle weakness   ☐ Muscle stiffness   ☐ Muscle aches

☐ Headache   ☐ Brain fog   ☐ Forgetfulness

☐ _____   ☐ _____

☐ _____   ☐ _____

Other symptoms:

_____

_____

WHAT ABOUT YOUR...?   **Feeling sick?**

Mood   ① ② ③ ④ ⑤ ⑥ ⑦ ⑧ ⑨ ⑩   ☐   Nope!

Energy levels   ① ② ③ ④ ⑤ ⑥ ⑦ ⑧ ⑨ ⑩   ☐   Yes...

Mental clarity   ① ② ③ ④ ⑤ ⑥ ⑦ ⑧ ⑨ ⑩

☐ Nausea   ☐ Diarrhea   ☐ Vomiting   ☐ Sore throat

☐ Congestion   ☐ Coughing   ☐ Chills   ☐ Fever

Other symptoms: _____

LAST NIGHT'S SLEEP

Hours of Sleep (1) (2) (3) (4) (5) (6) (7) (8) (9) (10) (+)

Sleep Quality (1) (2) (3) (4) (5) (6) (7) (8) (9) (10)

STRESS LEVELS

None	Low	Medium	High	Max	@$#%!

FOOD / MEDICATIONS

food / drinks	meds / supplements	time	dose

☐ usual daily medication

water ⟹ (1) (2) (3) (4) (5) (6) (7) (8) (9) (10)

caffeine ⟹ (1) (2) (3) (4) (5) (6) (7) (8) (9) (10)

alcohol ⟹ (1) (2) (3) (4) (5) (6) (7) (8) (9) (10)

EXERCISE / DAILY ACTIVITY

☐ Heck yes, I worked out.

☐ I managed to exercise a bit.

☐ No, I haven't exercised at all.

☐ I did some stuff, and that counts.

DETAILS

NOTES / TRIGGERS / IMPROVEMENTS

I AM GRATEFUL FOR...

Notes

Made in United States
North Haven, CT
02 May 2022

18824178R00075